Walk in Space

The Story of Project Gemini

Could two spaceships maneuver precisely enough to rendezvous in outer space and then dock together?

Could American spacemen move and work in the extreme conditions of outer space, away from the protection of a spacecraft?

Project Gemini was planned to answer these questions—questions which had to be answered if Americans were ever to go to the moon.

Continuing the story he began in *Americans into Orbit: The Story of Project Mercury*, Gene Gurney now tells about the courageous Gemini astronauts and their exciting missions.

Walk in Space

The Story of Project Gemini

by Gene Gurney

Illustrated with photographs

Random House · New York

Library of Congress Catalog Card Number 67-17179

Manufactured in the United States of America

Designed by William Lahey Cummings

All photographs in this book are from the National Aeronautics and Space Administration.

Contents

Walk in Space

The Story of Project Gemini

CHAPTER 1
A Human Satellite

On June 3, 1965, millions of Americans listening to their radios or watching TV heard these words: "This is Gemini Control. Four hours and twenty-four minutes into the mission. The Hawaii station has just established contact and the pilot, Jim McDivitt, advises the cabin has been depressurized. It is reading zero. We are standing by for a GO from Hawaii to open the hatch. . . . White has opened the door. He has stood up, and it's a most relaxed period. McDivitt reports that White is standing in the seat."

One hundred and twenty miles above the surface of the earth, Edward H. White II, one of the astronauts in the National Aeronautics and Space Administration's Project Gemini program, was about to take a walk in space!

Astronaut White's big adventure had actually begun almost a year earlier, on July 27, 1964, when he and Astronaut James A. McDivitt were told that they would be pilot and command pilot respectively for Gemini 4. Project Mercury, America's first manned space-flight program, had sent only one astronaut into space at a time. But Project Gemini used a spaceship big enough to carry two men. The name Gemini is the one astronomers have given to the twin stars Castor and Pollux, and NASA adopted it for the space program that would send "space twins" into orbit around the earth.

During the months before June, 1965, Astronauts McDivitt and White practiced again and again for every part of their historic space journey. They did this with the help of special rooms and of machines called simulators, which reproduce on the ground the conditions of space flight. In a pressure chamber that simulated the conditions found 150,000 feet above the earth, Astronaut White received special drill in unsealing a spacecraft hatch and putting his head through the opening.

A backup crew consisting of Astronauts Frank Borman and James A. Lovell, Jr., participated in every phase of the preflight training. If, for medical or other reasons, McDivitt and White were unable to make the trip on June 3, Borman and Lovell would go in their places. However, when McDivitt and White finished the thorough physical examinations two days before the flight, the astronauts' chief physician, Dr. Charles Berry, reported that they were perfectly fit.

On Launch Pad 19 at Cape Kennedy on Florida's east

Astronaut McDivitt trains for his flight in the Gemini Mission Simulator.

coast, a Gemini spacecraft had been installed on top of
a gleaming, 90-foot-tall Titan 2 missile. Early in the morning on June 3, before Astronauts McDivitt and White were
awake, Pad 19 was humming with activity. Workers were
busy on the ground and in the Gemini control room. Borman and Lovell were supervising preparations in the White
Room, at the top of the gantry that surrounded the Gemini
spacecraft and the Titan. This was the special dust-free
room from which the space capsule would be entered. The
White Room was kept absolutely clean to prevent dust
particles from getting into the spacecraft's mechanisms
and causing false readings on its delicate instruments.

Command Pilot McDivitt and Pilot White were awakened at 4:30 A.M., four and a half hours before their space
flight was scheduled to begin, or T minus 4 hours, 30 minutes. First each man received a final medical examination.
This was followed by a breakfast of tomato juice, broiled
steak, poached eggs, toast, strawberry gelatin, and coffee.

After breakfast the astronauts took a short ride to the
"ready room" on Pad 16. In the ready room, technicians
placed medical sensors on the two astronauts. During the
space flight the sensors would relay information on the
astronauts' physical condition. Next, silvery spacesuits were
donned, adjusted, and checked.

Because he would be leaving the spaceship while in
orbit, White wore a special suit with extra layers of material for protection against heat and micrometeoroids. His
helmet had two external visors: a tinted outer visor to re-
duce glare, and an inner visor of Lexan, coated to prevent
heat leak from inside the suit. (Lexan is a plastic which

is 30 times stronger than the plastic used in aircraft canopies.)

During their stay at Pad 16 both men spent some time breathing pure oxygen through a face mask. This preoxygenation, which removed all traces of nitrogen from their bodies, was part of the preparations for space flight.

Although the air we breathe consists of approximately 80 per cent nitrogen and 20 per cent oxygen, only oxygen is necessary to sustain life. To save weight and space, the Gemini capsules were pressurized with pure oxygen. However, before the astronauts opened the spacecraft's hatch, they would depressurize their capsule until there was a vacuum inside similar to the vacuum outside in space. The astronauts' suits would remain pressurized with oxygen, of course. But if one of the suits developed a leak, or if the oxygen supply to the suits failed, the astronauts would experience a sudden and severe drop in pressure. Any nitrogen in their bodies would form bubbles, causing the astronauts to develop decompression illness. This would also happen during normal space flight if cabin pressure dropped suddenly. Deep-sea divers who come to the surface too rapidly often get decompression illness, which they call the "bends."

The next stop for McDivitt and White was Pad 19. Busy technicians paused to watch as the two astronauts, carrying the portable air conditioners that cooled their spacesuits, marched up a short red ramp to an elevator that lifted them to the White Room. At 7:12 they entered the spacecraft, McDivitt taking the command pilot's position on the left and White the position on the right.

McDivitt (front) and White settle into lift-off position while White Room technicians hover around.

Nearly 1,000 miles away, at NASA's Manned Spacecraft Center in Houston, Texas, Gemini's flight director, Christopher Columbus Kraft, Jr., was following the activity at Pad 19 with the help of more than one hundred instrument consoles and giant display screens. His Houston Control Center was in constant contact with Cape Kennedy's control room. Once the spacecraft was in orbit, control of the mission would switch from Cape Kennedy to Houston.

In addition to the control centers at Houston and Cape Kennedy, a world-wide network of tracking stations waited to monitor the flight with the help of radar and radio. The network included ships at sea as well as land stations in Bermuda; the Canary Islands; Ascension, an island in the South Atlantic; Kano, Nigeria; Tananarive, Malagasy Republic; Carnarvon, Australia; Woomera, Australia; Canton Island in the South Pacific; Hawaii; Point Arguello, California; Guaymas, Mexico; White Sands, New Mexico; Corpus Christi, Texas; and Eglin Air Force Base in Florida.

Gemini 4's route was planned to pass over the tracking stations, where highly trained technicians were prepared to collect data on the orbiting spacecraft and its occupants for transmission to Houston or other points in the Gemini network. At most stations one man—called a capsule, or ground, communicator—would be able to talk with the astronauts when Gemini 4 was within radio range. He would then give them directions, answer their questions, and help them with any problems that developed. In some cases the capsule communicator would be one of the other astronauts.

The launch of Gemini 4 was scheduled for 9 A.M. Eastern

Standard Time. By 7:35 A.M. the astronauts were inside the spacecraft, and its two hatches had been closed and secured. The countdown proceeded on schedule until less than an hour remained before launching. Then came the report: "T minus 34 minutes and 59 seconds and holding."

It was time for the gantry that surrounded the Titan 2 and the spacecraft to be lowered to a horizontal position, but the electrically controlled combination erector and service tower would not swing down. The hold lasted for an hour and 16 minutes while technicians worked on the problem. They found some switched wires in a junction box. At 9:41 the countdown was underway once more and there were no more holds. Gemini 4 was GO.

Lift-off, one of the most suspense-filled moments in any space flight, came at 10:16 A.M. At the base of the Titan 2 launch vehicle, nearly 100 feet below the astronauts, two powerful engines shot flames and noxious fumes over Pad 19. With a roar that could be heard for miles, the rocket began to move upward, carrying Gemini 4 with it.

Inside the space capsule the two astronauts felt the upward movement. "The clock is operating," Jim McDivitt reported. It was the astronauts' traditional signal for GO.

Astronaut Virgil I. Grissom, who was serving as Mission Control Communicator at the Manned Spacecraft Center in Houston, sent a cheerful message: "Everything looks great, Jim."

"Beautiful, beautiful," McDivitt replied.

A multiple exposure shows the final countdown sequence of gantry lowering and Titan-Gemini lift-off.

Two minutes and 36 seconds after the lift-off, the first stage of the Titan 2 rocket shut down. It dropped off, and the one-engine second stage took over. In Houston, Flight Director Kraft was carefully following Gemini 4's progress. The spaceship's trajectory, or path, had to be exactly right or the ship would not go into the proper orbit. Soon Houston was announcing happily: "The trajectory plot is right on the line, both in lofting and all other elements. We're right on the money."

As its flight path had indicated it would, the Titan carried the spacecraft into the planned orbit at 10:22 A.M., just six minutes after lift-off. Two minutes later Command Pilot McDivitt reported that the spaceship had separated from the burned-out second stage of the rocket. But despite his best efforts to remain within a few hundred feet of the booster, it began to tumble and fall away. This was bad news. Near the end of the first orbit, McDivitt planned to guide Gemini 4 to within 20 feet of the booster, and during his space walk Astronaut White would approach it. If the rocket was tumbling, both maneuvers would be difficult and dangerous.

At the moment, however, the two astronauts were enjoying the experience of being weightless in space as Gemini 4 sped over the Atlantic Ocean and Africa and entered the first of the 66 "nights" that it would encounter in the next few days.

With the coming of darkness McDivitt and White could see the bright strobe beacons carried by the 27-foot sec-

The eastern tip of the Arabian peninsula, as seen from Gemini 4. The wrinkles at lower left are sand dunes.

ond stage of the Titan. "The light is working fine," Mc-
Divitt reported to the tracking station at Carnarvon,
Australia. "But I can't tell exactly how far away I am
from it."

Carnarvon suggested that McDivitt employ Gemini 4's
orbital attitude and maneuvering system (OAMS) to bring
the spacecraft closer to the booster. The maneuvering
system had 16 small rocket engines, or thrusters, located
at the sides and base of the adapter section. These could
be used to speed up the spacecraft, slow it down, move
it sideways in space, or move it up or down. The system's
rockets also controlled the spacecraft's attitude, or posture,
in space by regulating its rolling motion, its pitch (the
height of its blunt end), and its yaw (motion around its
vertical axis).

McDivitt followed Carnarvon's instructions, but he could
not move closer to the Titan. He finally had to settle
for just keeping it in sight.

The 45-minute "night" ended as the astronauts crossed
the Pacific Ocean. They had already reached the highest
point in their orbital path—183 miles above the surface
of the earth. It was a record altitude for United States
space flights. They had a GO from Mission Control for a
minimum of three orbits, and Dr. Berry had cleared White
for extravehicular activity, or EVA in the language of
space.

When McDivitt established contact with the tracking
station at Guaymas, Mexico, he reported: "We still have
the booster. We're out quite a way from it now. It's
taken a little more fuel than we'd anticipated. We appear

right now to be holding our own with it. Of course, we should start to close with it, but it's further than we'd hoped to let it get, right now."

McDivitt resumed his efforts to guide Gemini 4 toward the Titan. Then he called Guaymas again: "Guaymas, this is Gemini Four. We're going to have to get resolution right away on whether we really make a major effort to close the thing or save fuel."

From Guaymas came the answer. "I think we should save the fuel."

Mission Control at Houston had been monitoring the conversation between McDivitt and Guaymas. Out of direct contact with the spaceship but able to communicate with the tracking station at Guaymas, Mission Control suggested: "You might tell him as far as we're concerned, we want to save the fuel."

The approach to the Titan 2 booster was to have been America's first attempt at a rendezvous in space. When McDivitt received the message from Houston he was disappointed. "I guess we are just going to watch it go away," he said. But he agreed that the decision to save fuel was a wise one: "I'd like to save enough to help bring me down. I don't want to get down to wherever it's going." McDivitt was referring to the booster's fiery future: the rocket would eventually fall into the earth's atmosphere and burn up.

Meanwhile, Astronaut White had been busy with preparations for his space walk, which was scheduled for Gemini 4's second orbit. He had a list of some 40 things to do before he left the spacecraft. Some gear had to be stowed away, other gear had to be unpacked, and switches had to be set. White's equipment began to fill up the small cabin and McDivitt radioed to Houston: "It's a bit crowded in here."

As Gemini 4 approached the tracking station in Hawaii on its second orbit, Ed White realized that he would not reach the end of his checklist in time. McDivitt told Hawaii: "We'll wait until the next pass around. . . . I don't think we want to try it this time."

From Houston, Flight Director Kraft relayed his approval: "Tell Jim we are happy with that decision."

When Gemini 4 passed over Australia for the third time, McDivitt was able to report: "It's GO for EVA."

The capsule communicator at Carnarvon responded with permission to start decompression of the spacecraft. McDivitt opened a vent and began letting air out of the cabin. The astronauts' spacesuits had already been filled with compensating oxygen from pressurized bottles. When the hatch was opened to let White out, both astronauts would be in the near vacuum of outer space, but their pressure suits would protect them.

Then, from the spacecraft speeding high over Hawaii came the message millions of people had been waiting for: "He's ready to egress right now."

At this point the Hawaii tracking station lost contact with Gemini 4 as the spacecraft moved out of range. Four minutes of silence followed while anxious space officials in Hawaii called: "Gemini Four, Hawaii Cap Com. Can you repeat your last transmission? Do you copy?"

There was no answer, and the worried nation waited. Had something gone wrong? Had Astronaut White been able to leave the space capsule?

When the tracking station at Guaymas finally reached Gemini 4, White had indeed left the orbiting space capsule. Clad in his 21-pound spacesuit with an American flag on the left shoulder, the astronaut had become a satellite of the earth, like Gemini 4 itself. White still retained a connection with the spacecraft, however—a combination air hose, communications line, and nylon tether, 25 feet long and gold-colored to reflect heat.

In his right hand America's first space walker carried a maneuvering unit which the astronauts called "the gun." By pressing two triggers White could release compressed oxygen through a system of nozzles and propel himself in whatever direction he wanted to go.

After maneuvering himself out of the spacecraft with the gun, he had moved off—to the bottom of Gemini 4 and back to the top of the adapter, the unit that had connected the spacecraft to its booster. White tried to use the gun sparingly, but soon he had to report: "The maneuvering unit is good. The only problem is that I haven't got enough fuel. I've exhausted the fuel now."

Brief as it was, his experiment with the maneuvering unit had made Edward White the first self-propelled astronaut in orbit. Soviet Cosmonaut Alexei Leonov had had no such device during his ten-minute space walk on March 18, 1965.

With no more fuel in his gun, White began to use his tether to guide his movements. In addition to testing the

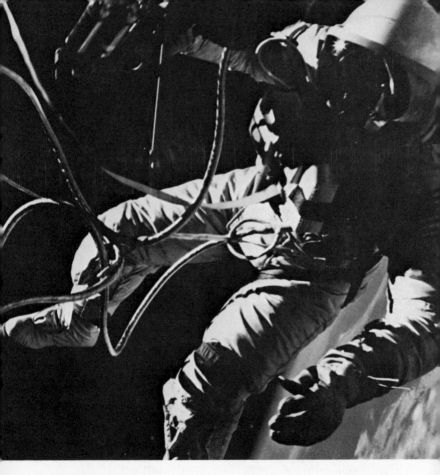

Holding his maneuvering gun, Astronaut White floats in space. His chest pack contains an emergency oxygen supply.

gun, NASA wanted to find out if the tether could be used to guide an astronaut as well as to supply him with oxygen and carry his messages.

Ed White later reported: "The tether was quite useful. I was able to go right back where I started every time, but I wasn't able to maneuver to specific points with it. . . . I also used it to pull myself down to the space-craft, and at one time I called down and said: 'I am actually walking across the top of the spacecraft,' and that is exactly what I was doing. I took the tether to give myself a little friction on the top of the spacecraft and walked about three or four steps until the angle of the tether to the spacecraft got so much that my feet went out from under me."

Astronaut White also pointed out: "I realized right away that our tether was mounted so that it put me ex-actly where I was told to stay out of." McDivitt had told him to stay away from the adapter end and also the thruster firings.

With Ed White moving about outside and Jim McDivitt keeping the spacecraft in a stable attitude to give White a constant point of reference, Gemini 4 floated, nose downward, across the United States. It passed over San Diego, Phoenix, Houston, New Orleans, the Gulf of Mex-ico, and out over the Atlantic once more.

The two astronauts took pictures, discussed the extra-ordinary view, and remarked on the joys of space travel. Occasionally they remembered to send a message to the ground. From above Houston McDivitt radioed: "We're looking right down at you." A few seconds later he asked Virgil Grissom at Mission Control: "Got any message for us?"

At Mission Control, Flight Director Kraft had been watching the clock. According to the Gemini 4 flight plan, White was to stay outside the spacecraft for 12 minutes. The 12 minutes were up and Mission Control had been trying to contact the two orbiting astronauts.

Grissom's message for them was a short one: "Gemini Four. Get back in!"

When informed of the order to return to the spacecraft, White, who was enjoying every minute of his space walk, protested: "I'm just fine."

McDivitt's answer to that was: "No, back in. Come on." Finally he told the reluctant space walker: "We've got three and a half more days to go, buddy."

With an "I'm coming," White maneuvered himself to the top of the capsule. After handing his camera to the waiting McDivitt, he prepared to lower himself through the open hatch. "It's the saddest moment of my life," he said at the end of his 23 minutes outside the space capsule.

Inside the spacecraft, McDivitt helped reel in the gold tether. To Houston's query about how things were going, he replied: "He's standing in the seat now and his legs are down below the instrument panel. He's coming in."

Before settling down into his seat for the remainder of the space voyage, White had to close and secure the open hatch door. When he attempted to seal the hatch, the ratchet handle moved loosely in his hand. The hatch wasn't sealing. It was a bad moment. The two astronauts couldn't survive for long with an unsealed hatch. However, their training had included a lesson on malfunctioning hatch doors. They pulled and tugged and manipulated gears until the hatches snapped shut. McDivitt then re-pressurized the cabin and reported: "Everything's fine. . . . We're feeling great."

CHAPTER 2
A Very Successful Flight

Project Gemini's first attempt to carry out extravehicular activity had been very successful. And it was not a stunt. The future development of America's space program depended on the ability of astronauts to maneuver in space outside a spacecraft.

EVA was over, but many hours of flight lay ahead of Gemini 4. They were to be busy hours for the two astronauts, who had 11 medical, engineering, and scientific experiments to carry out. First, however, White was advised to take a four-hour nap. He later reported that he "slept some, but not sound." McDivitt was scheduled for a four-hour sleep period when White awakened. Gemini 4's flight plan called for each man to sleep eight hours of each 24 in two periods of four hours each.

The two astronauts continued their space trip in a cluttered cabin. Although only one space walk was programmed for Gemini 4, it had been hoped that the spaceship could be depressurized again, the hatch opened, and unneeded equipment tossed overboard. The 25-foot tether that had connected White with the spaceship during his walk and other items he had used were to be disposed of in this way. After their trouble closing the hatch at the conclusion of the space walk, however, the astronauts were advised by Mission Control not to "crack the hatches" again.

"We have most of that junk down in the foot well and I guess . . . we're going to have to hold it," McDivitt said.

During their second day in space, Flight Director Kraft told the astronauts that they could use their orbital attitude and maneuvering system (OAMS) when the flight plan called for it. They had tried to conserve maneuvering fuel since their failure to rendezvous with the second stage of the Titan 2 booster. OAMS now moved the spacecraft into different orbits and in different directions with its small rocket engines.

On the afternoon of the second day, during the nineteenth orbit, McDivitt was allowing the capsule to drift freely when, in the distance, he saw an object with "big arms sticking out." The startled astronaut took both still and motion pictures, but the glare of the sun made it impossible for him to identify the object. What was it? Probably one of the many hundreds of things now in orbit around the earth—the result of American and Russian space shots.

When McDivitt saw the satellite it was 6:30 P.M. EST and Gemini 4 was over South America. The official United States space-tracking registry indicates that ten objects were within 600 miles of Gemini 4 then. Pegasus 2, a large satellite with wing-like extensions that NASA had launched to study micrometeoroids, would have looked very much like what McDivitt saw as it traveled in space, but Pegasus 2 was 1,250 miles away from Gemini 4. The astronaut's film, when it was developed, only added to the mystery. It showed nothing that looked like a satellite.

Astronaut McDivitt was not the first man to see another satellite while traveling in space. That honor goes to Soviet Cosmonaut Alexei Leonov, who was also the first man to walk in space. During his 24-hour trip, he too saw an orbiting object that he couldn't identify. And before Gemini 4 landed, Astronaut McDivitt was to see two more, both of them small and far away.

While scientists on the ground consulted their charts and computers in an attempt to determine just what McDivitt did see, the astronauts in Gemini 4 continued their journey. As they circled the earth once every 94 minutes, they looked down upon roads, airport runways, ships' wakes, and sparkling city lights. Both astronauts were surprised at how much they could identify from their orbiting spaceship.

One of the things NASA wanted to learn from Gemini 4 was what effect long periods of weightlessness would have on space travelers. McDivitt and White were to travel around the earth more times than any of America's previous space travelers. Would the astronauts lose much

calcium and other minerals from their bones? This happens to people who are inactive for several days—when they are sick in bed, for example. If it happened to the astronauts, future travelers might have to worry about breaking weakened bones during any strenuous activity in space flight.

During McDivitt's and White's preflight physical examinations, doctors had taken special x-rays of the heel bone and of the end bone of the fifth finger on the right hand of each astronaut. They had also recorded blood pressures, pulse rates, and many other facts about the astronauts' physical condition. After the flight, another examination would determine if there had been any changes. And during the flight, space doctors received a steady flow of information from the sensors on such things as the astronauts' pulse and respiration rates.

Four meals, low in residue, or undigestible fiber, were part of the astronauts' carefully planned daily schedule. The calorie count—about 2500 a day—approximated their normal intake on earth. The meals differed slightly for each man. For example, Astronaut McDivitt on his third day in space ate a breakfast of sugar-frosted flakes, a double serving of bacon squares, cinnamon toast, and a mixture of orange and grapefruit juice. Astronaut White's menu was the same except that he had sausage patties instead of bacon.

For lunch McDivitt had tuna salad, a cheese sandwich, apricot pudding, and orange juice. White chose beef and

An enlarged detail of a Gemini 4 photo shows Cape Kennedy jutting into the Atlantic (looking southwest).

gravy instead of the tuna salad. During the rest of the day they ate the same foods. Their supper was cold pot roast, green peas, toasted bread cubes, pineapple cubes, and tea. And for their fourth and last meal of the day, the astronauts had chicken bites, toast, applesauce, brownies, and grapefruit juice.

Meals for the space trip were packed in 18 packages —14 two-man meals and four one-man meals. The packages, marked by day and meal, were connected by a nylon cord to keep them in the proper order in case they floated about inside the compartment where they were stored. The food was bite-sized and usually dehydrated or freeze-dried. Before eating the dehydrated and some of the freeze-dried items, the astronauts added water with a special water gun.

Each of the packages of freeze-dried food contained a disinfectant tablet which the astronauts could later replace in the package to prevent the spoilage of any left-over food.

For the astronauts, life in space settled down to a routine of eating, sleeping, taking pictures, and conducting experiments. Sometimes, however, the routine was broken by special news from home. The astronauts were told the scores of the Little League games in which their sons played, and both men talked with their wives.

Another diversion occurred when Gemini 4 passed over Australia on its forty-fourth orbit. The city of Melbourne turned on its lights and the astronauts were able to see some of them through the clouds. McDivitt radioed the Carnarvon tracking station: "Tell them I thank them for lighting the night for me."

So it went until the forty-eighth orbit, with 14 orbits yet to go. During that orbit trouble developed in Gemini 4's computer. The astronauts were planning to use the computer to help them control the reëntry of the space-craft into the earth's atmosphere, but the computer's on-off switch seemed to be stuck in the "on" position. Astronaut White reported: "It's impossible to put any-thing in . . . and when we go to turn the computer off and come back on it . . . I still get the malfunction light on in a second or two."

During the ensuing orbits, the astronauts and Gemini officials on the ground tried to discover what was wrong with the computer. Finally, the effort was abandoned. Gemini 4 would have to come down from space without the help of a computer. This meant that instead of being guided down by the astronauts, it would make a ballistic reëntry. Ballistics is the science that deals with the motion of bullets and other projectiles. When Gemini 4 reëntered the earth's atmosphere, its path would resemble the path that a bullet follows when it falls back to earth. The Project Mercury space capsule had used the ballistic reëntry method, but a different system had been worked out for Project Gemini.

The Gemini capsule had been built with an offset center of gravity. This would cause air to move unevenly over its surface as it descended, producing the same kind of lift that an airplane gets. By using information from the on-board computer, a Gemini astronaut could control the capsule's lift and "fly" it down to a designated land-

The Houston Control Room

during a Gemini mission.

ing point. Astronauts McDivitt and White would not be able to "fly" Gemini 4 down, however.

In the Atlantic, the carrier *Wasp*, primary recovery vessel for the Gemini 4 space flight, moved 148 miles to the west. Because Gemini 4 could not be guided down, its landing area had changed. In addition to the *Wasp*, 21 other ships, 88 Air Force and Navy airplanes, and 15,000 people were deployed around the world to pick up the two astronauts no matter where they landed. The bulk of the recovery force was concentrated in the Atlantic where Gemini 4 was now expected to land, about 500 miles southwest of Bermuda.

Mission Control sent Gemini 4 preliminary landing instructions during the fifty-fifth orbit and relayed a weather report for the recovery area: "Good visibility with waves three to four feet high."

The two astronauts continued their eat-sleep-work routine for five more orbits. Then they concentrated on getting ready to return to earth. All of their gear had to be carefully stowed away because its location affected the balance of the spacecraft. In addition, any loose articles might fly around in the small cabin and strike the astronauts when Gemini 4 reëntered the earth's atmosphere and weightlessness ended.

Reëntry began over Hawaii during the sixty-second orbit when the astronauts fired two maneuvering rockets and lowered the spacecraft's orbit. Twelve minutes later, over Mexico, they fired four retro-rockets to take Gemini 4 out of orbit. These were crucial steps. A mistake in handling the maneuvering rockets could send Gemini 4 into a higher orbit. If the retro-rockets fired early or late, Gemini 4 would come down many miles away from the recovery forces.

After McDivitt reported that the retro-rockets had been fired, Mission Control made some rapid computer calculations and told him that the landing would be 40 to 50 miles west of the planned recovery area. This was close enough to the *Wasp* for its helicopters to pick up the two astronauts.

Gemini 4 was now hurtling toward the earth, turning into a fireball as it rushed through the thickening air. For four minutes, while temperatures on the spacecraft's heat shield reached as high as 3,000 degrees Fahrenheit, no messages came from the spacecraft and none could be received by it. When communications were resumed, McDivitt reported that he could hear the radio of the *Wasp* "loud and clear."

Its descent slowed by a high-altitude drogue parachute and then by an 84-foot main parachute, Gemini 4 settled into the Atlantic Ocean at 12:12 P.M. EST on Monday, June 7. Its four-day space journey had taken it around the earth 62 times and set a new United States record— 97 hours, 59 minutes, and 11 seconds in space.

While the *Wasp* raced toward the point of touchdown, its helicopters flew ahead to look for Gemini 4. Within minutes one of them had located the capsule bobbing in the Atlantic. The helicopter hovered overhead, sometimes no more than ten feet above the spacecraft, and three Navy frogmen jumped into the water. They fixed a bright flotation collar around Gemini 4. Then the two astro-

White and McDivitt are welcomed aboard the Wasp.

nauts emerged from the capsule and jumped into a life raft. After the astronauts had splashed their faces with water, they were lifted to the twin-jet recovery helicopter —first McDivitt and then White. The helicopter carried them to the *Wasp*, where they received a joyous welcome from the ship's crew.

Later, Gemini 4 was hoisted aboard the *Wasp*. The technicians who examined it found that the spaceship was in excellent shape after its 1,600,000-mile journey.

The astronauts too were in excellent shape. After their arrival on the *Wasp*, they had gone to the ship's sick bay to start a series of physical examinations. The doctors on the *Wasp* reported: "No complications."

When asked about the effects of the flight on the two astronauts, Dr. Berry predicted that Gemini 4 would "knock down an awful lot of straw men." He explained that he was referring to the theory that "we might have a couple of unconscious astronauts on our hands." Neither McDivitt nor White had shown symptoms of light-headedness. Their blood pressures were lower than usual when they landed and their pulse rates were 10 to 30 points higher. Twenty-four hours later the astronauts' pulse rates were nearly normal again, and within a few days their blood pressures were normal too. X-rays taken on the *Wasp* and 16 days and 50 days after the landing showed that the astronauts did lose small quantities of calcium and other minerals from their bones, but the loss was not a permanent one.

The medics were not the only ones pleased with the space flight. At the Manned Spacecraft Center, Dr. George

E. Mueller, head of NASA's manned-flight program, summed it up: "We are all tremendously pleased with the results of the Gemini Four flight. Gemini Four was one of the most successful missions in our manned spaceflight program."

With the exception of the rendezvous with the second stage of the Titan 2 booster, Gemini 4 had accomplished the objectives set for it. Two men and their supporting equipment had been tested for four days in space. An astronaut had successfully performed extravehicular activity. Several valuable experiments had been carried out. And the spacecraft and its occupants had returned safely to earth.

As for Astronauts Jim McDivitt and Ed White, they were so pleased with their trip into space that they announced they would like to go again.

CHAPTER 3
Project Gemini:
A Step to the Moon

The successful journey of Gemini 4 was the eighth manned flight in the United States space program. Seven other American astronauts had traveled in space before Jim McDivitt and Ed White. They were Alan B. Shepard, Jr., Virgil I. Grissom, John H. Glenn, Jr., Malcolm Scott Carpenter, Walter M. Schirra, Jr., Gordon Cooper, and John W. Young. All were Project Mercury astronauts except John Young, whose first space flight had been in Gemini 3. Virgil Grissom accompanied him on that flight, becoming the first astronaut to travel in space twice.

Project Mercury was America's first manned space-flight program. It got under way in August, 1958, soon after the National Aeronautics and Space Act of 1958 created the National Aeronautics and Space Administration, or NASA.

It took the pioneering Project Mercury almost three

years to develop the equipment for manned space flight and to train a group of seven astronauts. Then, on May 5, 1961, Project Mercury Astronaut Alan Shepard made a successful suborbital flight—up into space and back down again without going into orbit around the earth. Astronaut Virgil Grissom made a similar flight on July 21, 1961.

America's first manned orbital flight took place on February 20, 1962, when John Glenn traveled around the earth three times. Scott Carpenter duplicated that feat on May 24, 1962. Later in 1962, on October 2, Walter Schirra made a six-orbit flight, and on May 15-16, 1963, Gordon Cooper remained in space for 22 orbits.

With Astronaut Cooper's flight, Project Mercury came to an end. It had successfully accomplished its objectives —to place manned space capsules in orbital flight around the earth; to learn some basic facts about the effects of space travel on astronauts; and to bring the astronauts and their capsules safely back to earth.

In 1961, when Project Mercury's manned flights were just getting under way, President John F. Kennedy announced a new space goal for the United States. It was to land a man on the moon and return him safely back to earth before the end of the 1960s. For a country that had not yet put a man into orbit around the earth, this was an ambitious program indeed.

As it happened, NASA's plans for the future already included a manned expedition to the moon, though without such an early deadline. NASA called it Project Apollo. A lunar expedition would be very expensive and NASA had received only limited funds for work on Project Apollo. After the President's announcement, however, Project Apollo was adopted as the nation's new space goal and more funds became available.

Manned exploration of the moon would be much more difficult than anything planned for Project Mercury. It would require an elaborate spacecraft with room for three astronauts. After the spacecraft carried the three astronauts into a lunar orbit, a landing vehicle would leave the spacecraft to take two astronauts to the surface of the moon. The astronauts would explore the moon and use the landing vehicle to return to the orbiting spacecraft. Then the spacecraft would come back to earth.

In January, 1962, NASA announced a new space program to bridge the gap between Project Mercury and Project Apollo—Project Gemini. Project Gemini spacecraft would stay in orbit for a week or longer. And Project Gemini astronauts would practice linking their spacecraft with another orbiting object. Both the ability to make long flights and the ability to rendezvous and dock in space were very important to the success of Project Apollo.

Because of the length of the flights planned for Project Gemini, NASA decided to use two-man crews in the new space program. Then one man could sleep while the other managed the spacecraft. Also, one man alone might not be able to perform the difficult rendezvous maneuver.

The seven Project Mercury astronauts would eventually move over to Project Gemini, but NASA needed more than seven men to carry out the two-man flights and, later, the three-man flights of Project Apollo. In September, 1962, therefore, a second group of nine astronauts joined the original seven. Like the Mercury astronauts before them, they were carefully chosen from among the nation's top test pilots. A third group of 14 astronauts was selected in October, 1963.

All of the men were college graduates. Some of them had advanced degrees in science or aeronautical engineering. They had also completed pilot and test pilot training, but many more hours of training lay ahead of them.

The new astronauts studied astronautics and related subjects. They traveled to jungles, deserts, and mountains to learn firsthand what to do if their spaceships came down in such terrain. They also learned how to survive at sea if they landed far away from the ships and planes waiting to pick them up.

Engineers and scientists have developed special rooms that duplicate some of the conditions found in space. In one of these, called an altitude chamber, the astronauts underwent the same decrease in air pressure that they would later encounter when traveling into space. Another chamber duplicated the zero g, or absence of gravity, that they would experience in space.

In addition to their general preparation for space flight, the astronauts spent many hours in trainers especially developed for Project Gemini. These trainers duplicated the systems of a space capsule. In a trainer called the Gemini Mission Simulator, the men practiced all of the things that an astronaut would do during a Gemini flight. They also practiced the procedures to be followed in case of an

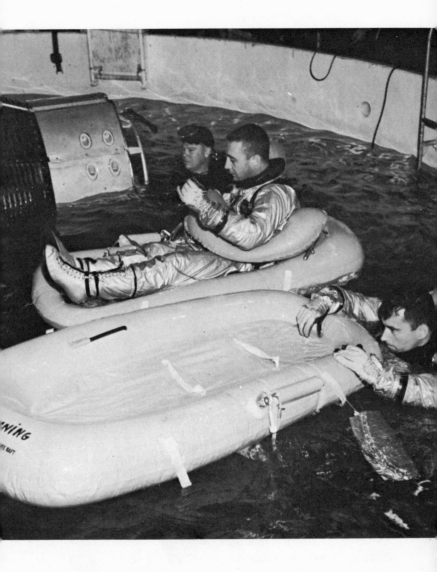

Astronauts Grissom (on raft) and Young learn how to leave a capsule after splashdown.

Training at zero gravity: Neil Armstrong emerges from a Gemini mock-up and David Scott practices maneuvering while weightless.

emergency during a space flight. In other trainers, called part-task trainers, they practiced the rendezvous and docking maneuvers that they would later perform in space as Gemini astronauts.

While the astronauts were training, work was under way on the spaceship in which they would ride. Instead of developing a totally new capsule for Project Gemini, NASA decided to use a two-man version of the Project Mercury capsule. There were some changes, of course. The Gemini capsule was larger, for one thing. It was a foot higher, a foot and a half wider at the base, and it had about 50 per cent more cabin space. The 16-foot escape tower that stood on top of the Mercury capsule was eliminated. Gemini crews would use ejection seats if they had to escape from the spacecraft. And for Gemini, some of the spacecraft's equipment was arranged differently. Components that didn't have to be located within the pressurized crew cabin were placed in two bays between the capsule's pressurized section and its outer shell. Large doors enabled technicians to reach the equipment easily when repairs were needed.

Perhaps the biggest change in the Gemini spacecraft was the addition of an adapter section. It connected the 90-inch-wide capsule with the 120-inch-wide booster. The adapter, in addition to serving as a connection, carried equipment for the operation of the capsule.

Because so much of the basic capsule and its equipment had already been tested in the course of Project Mercury, development of the Gemini spacecraft proceeded rapidly. The McDonnell Aircraft Corporation, the same company that built the Mercury capsule, received the Gemini contract for 13 flight-rated (tested and ready for use) capsules. McDonnell delivered the first one to NASA on October 4, 1963.

Like the Gemini spacecraft, the Gemini launch vehicle had already undergone considerable testing because NASA chose the Air Force's Titan 2 for Gemini. NASA liked the Titan's simplified mechanical and electrical systems and the fact that it used a hypergolic fuel. A hypergolic fuel is one that ignites spontaneously when it comes into contact with an oxidizer. In the case of the Titan 2, the fuel is a mixture of unsymmetrical-dimethyl hydrazine and monomethyl hydrazine. The oxidizer is nitrogen tetroxide.

The Air Force had developed the Titan as an intercontinental ballistic missile. It was designed to travel to a military target thousands of miles away from the United States. On such a trip it would carry explosives in its nose compartment. When working for NASA, however, its powerful engines would lift the three-ton Gemini space capsule into orbit around the earth.

Before the Titan 2 became the Gemini launch vehicle, it underwent some changes. Engineers modified the nose of the missile to fit the spacecraft's adapter. And they added some extra equipment. One of the additions was a malfunction-detection system to alert the flight crew to possible trouble during launching or flight. In another safety measure, the booster's most important systems were duplicated as a protection against failure. If a system broke down, its duplicate would automatically take over.

A Titan 2 is assembled on Pad 19. The second stage is being lifted into place by the gantry.

Unfortunately, the modified Titan didn't accelerate smoothly after launching. If uncorrected, its "pogo-stick action" would give the astronauts a very rough ride—rough enough to "shake the pilots' eyeballs out," as one NASA official put it. After engineers refined the Titan's fuel distribution system, the booster passed its tests and was declared ready for manned space flight. First, however, NASA sent up two unmanned Gemini flights to make sure that the booster and the spacecraft would work together.

Gemini 1, on April 8, 1964, was an almost completely successful flight. There were no holds during the count-down and the Titan 2 left Cape Kennedy's Pad 19 only one second behind schedule. But the Titan traveled 14 miles an hour too fast, sending the spacecraft 21 miles higher than it should have gone. This was a minor problem, however—one that astronauts could have corrected easily had they been aboard. As the first Gemini capsule orbited the earth, pleased space officials announced that the flight was "well within manned tolerances," meaning that astronauts could have survived the stresses of Gemini 1's acceleration without sustaining physical damage.

Four days later Gemini 1 reëntered the earth's atmosphere and disintegrated over the Atlantic Ocean between South America and Africa. The second stage of the Titan came down with it because no attempt had been made to separate the two. The six NASA tracking stations that monitored Gemini 1's journey reported that both the capsule and the booster had performed well in normal space flight.

One important question remained unanswered, however. What would have happened if the flight had not been a normal one? What if, for example, a pair of astronauts had to bring their spaceship down at the worst possible time—just before it went into orbit? Would the capsule and the astronauts be able to withstand the very high temperatures generated by the rapid fall back to earth? To find out, NASA scheduled the second unmanned Gemini flight for the fall of 1964. It was to be a suborbital shot in which dummy crewmen, installed on pallets instead of the regular pilots' couches, would occupy the spacecraft.

However, as it turned out, there were no more Gemini shots during 1964. First, on August 17 a severe electrical storm hit Cape Kennedy. On Pad 19 the Titan launch vehicle for Gemini 2 was already in place. The storm damaged part of its electrical system and some ground check-out equipment as well. Later that same month nature dealt Project Gemini another blow—this time in the form of a hurricane. On August 27 Hurricane Cleo battered Cape Kennedy with gale winds of 65 miles per hour. Fortunately, technicians had time to remove the second stage of the Titan from Pad 19. They tied down the larger first stage. No damage was done, but Gemini 2, already behind schedule because of the electrical storm, suffered a further postponement.

And that wasn't the end of the hard luck that dogged Gemini 2. In early September Hurricane Dora headed for the Florida coast with 125-mile-per-hour winds. Workers at Cape Kennedy decided to dismantle all the rockets on the pads except the giant Saturn 1SA-7. The Titan 2 on

Pad 19 was one of those removed, causing Gemini to be postponed again.

The much delayed Gemini 2 finally lifted off Pad 19 on January 19, 1965. After the launch, the space capsule traveled to an altitude of 98.9 miles before plunging back into the Atlantic where the carrier U.S.S. *Lake Champlain* was waiting to pick it up. Technicians who examined the capsule after its 19-minute trip into space and back announced that the heat-protection system had passed the test, as had the capsule's other systems. Nothing had happened to the dummy crewmen during reëntry. That was good news, for it meant that Project Gemini was ready to try a manned space flight.

At Cape Kennedy on January 19 two astronauts had followed the journey of Gemini 2 with special interest. They were Virgil I. Grissom and John W. Young, the pioneering command pilot and pilot of Gemini 3.

Astronaut Grissom was an experienced spaceman, having flown in a suborbital Project Mercury mission in 1961. When he landed in the Atlantic at the end of that flight, a hatch blew off his spacecraft, causing it to fill with water and sink. Astronaut Grissom almost went down too before a helicopter rescued him. In memory of that mishap, Grissom named his Gemini spacecraft "Molly Brown" after the heroine of a popular musical comedy, "The Unsinkable Molly Brown."

Molly Brown, with Grissom and Young aboard, left Pad 19 at 9:24 A.M. on March 23, 1965, after a countdown

Gemini 2 is hoisted aboard the Lake Champlain *after its successful flight.*

interrupted by only one short delay. As the Titan 2 booster lifted the capsule smoothly into space, Cape Kennedy radioed: "You're on your way, Molly Brown."

Never very talkative, Astronaut Grissom made only a brief reply. "Yeah, man," he said.

Inside the spacecraft the two astronauts, reclining on contour couches, clutched rings located between their knees. Their arms were pinned to their sides and their legs held by straps. If something went wrong during the launch, the astronauts would pull the rings and be ejected from the capsule, along with their seats, to return to earth by parachute.

At 15,000 feet, 50 seconds after lift-off, the astronauts let go of their rings and freed their limbs. They were now high enough to come down in the capsule if an emergency developed. But none did. Gemini 3 entered an orbit ranging from 100 to 140 miles high, and the two astronauts turned to their space duties.

Like many people on earth, the astronauts found that it was more pleasant to look out of the window than to work. Astronaut Young reported later: "There aren't words in the English language to describe the beauty. I was supposed to monitor the inertial guidance system . . . but it's just a tremendous effort to get your head back in the cockpit."

Both of the astronauts had a number of things to do during the flight. In addition to monitoring the spacecraft's systems, they observed various space phenomena and took part in experiments designed to measure the effects of space travel.

Astronaut Grissom carried out an important assignment

Astronaut Young strapped into lift-off position. The emergency ejection ring can be seen between his knees.

over Texas during the first orbit. He fired two 85-pound-thrust rockets directly into Gemini 3's flight path. The backward push of the rockets had a braking effect that slowed the spacecraft and gave it a new orbital path. This was the first time a manned spaceship had had the shape of its orbit changed in flight. "This was a big event, really a big event," Grissom said afterward.

Later, during the second orbit, the astronaut fired maneuvering rockets to change the plane, or tilt, of Gemini 3's orbit. At the end of the maneuver, the spacecraft's orbit was tilted at a slightly steeper angle in relation to the earth's equator. And during the spaceship's third journey around the earth, Grissom lowered the orbit's perigee, or low point, to 52 miles.

One very important maneuver lay ahead—reëntry. Gemini 3 was scheduled to come down at the end of the third orbit.

The reëntry procedure began with the jettisoning of part of the capsule's adapter section. Then, after Grissom fired four retro-rockets to slow the space capsule, the adapter section that held them was jettisoned also. With the firing of the retro-rockets, Gemini 3 started its downward plunge, picking up heat from the friction of the thickening atmosphere as it fell. The spacecraft's heat shield began to glow. Astronaut Young later described what he saw: "The first thing you notice is a sort of slight orange haze that envelops the spacecraft. And this haze layer increases and changes color to a dark green. It's a very beautiful thing. And then orange sparks of flaming material start flying upward."

In the Atlantic below the fiery Gemini 3, the recovery ship *Intrepid* waited. With the help of an on-board computer, Astronaut Grissom was going to try to guide Gemini 3 to a preselected landing area near the *Intrepid*. During the descent, the computer would tell him how to control the capsule's lift and, thus, its direction.

Before this flight, the amount of lift to be obtained from the stream of air rushing past the Gemini spacecraft during reëntry could only be estimated. As a result, the figures fed into the computer on Gemini 3 were inaccurate and the spacecraft came down 60 miles short of its target area. It settled into an Atlantic Ocean made choppy by a 20-knot wind, and for a moment the capsule's parachute dragged it along under the water. When Grissom released the parachute, the capsule popped to the surface and the two astronauts got a welcome glimpse of the sky through their hatch windows.

The capsule was watertight but far from stable in the rough Atlantic. Grissom became mildly seasick and both men were glad to leave the capsule for the rafts dropped by one of the recovery planes. A few minutes later a helicopter picked them up and carried them to the *Intrepid*.

Gemini's first manned flight had lasted four hours and 53 minutes—long enough to prove that the new space program was operational. Furthermore, the Gemini capsule's all-important maneuvering capability had been tested successfully. The United States was ready to move forward in its manned space-flight program.

CHAPTER 4
Eight Days in Space

When the first Americans travel to the moon, they will be gone about eight days. It will take them that long to reach the moon, briefly explore its surface, and return to earth.

Eight days is a long time to remain in space. In 1965 it was longer than anyone had ever spent there. A Soviet cosmonaut, Valery Bykovsky, had traveled in space for almost five days in 1963. The longest United States manned space flight was the one made by Astronauts Edward White and James McDivitt in Gemini 4, which lasted a little more than four days.

Could astronauts remain in space for as long as eight days without suffering damage to their health and efficiency? This was one of the most important things that space officials hoped to learn from Project Gemini. On August 21, 1965, they sent up the fifth Gemini capsule to obtain the answer.

Gemini 5 began as a "storybook mission," a term pilots use when everything goes exactly right. The spacecraft left Cape Kennedy precisely on schedule at 9 A.M. EST. The Titan 2 booster performed smoothly, as did all of the capsule's systems. From inside the capsule, Astronaut Gordon Cooper, the command pilot of Gemini 5, radioed his approval. "Feels mighty good," he said.

For Gordon, or Gordo, Cooper, Gemini 5 was the second space trip. In May, 1963, he made the last and longest Project Mercury flight. On that occasion he traveled around the earth 22 times in $34\frac{1}{2}$ hours.

With Cooper rode his copilot, Astronaut Charles Conrad. It was Conrad's first trip into space. Like all first-time space travelers, he was amazed at the view from the spacecraft. In his first message to the ground he exclaimed: "What a beautiful view!"

During Gemini 5's flight, in addition to testing the effects of eight days in space on themselves and their capsule, the two astronauts were going to conduct experiments and try out new equipment. Their spacecraft carried a new rendezvous radar device and a new fuel-cell power source.

It was the fuel cell that ended the storybook portion of Gemini 5's flight. Fuel cells are lighter than batteries and a better source of electrical power for long space voyages. They create electricity out of the energy that is released when two gases, hydrogen and oxygen, combine to form water. To operate, the fuel cell must receive a steady flow of both hydrogen and oxygen. Gemini 5 carried the hydrogen and oxygen in liquid form to save space. The liquid gases were stored in insulated containers, which kept them at the very low temperatures needed to maintain liquid form. The containers were fitted with heating elements to help turn the liquid hydrogen and oxygen back into gases before they were pumped into the fuel cell—a cavity divided down the middle by a plastic membrane. In the cell, the hydrogen passed through the membrane into the oxygen side and in the process produced an electric current.

The first indication that all was not well with the fuel cell came while Gemini 5 was passing over the Canary Islands during its second orbit of the earth. The data received from the spacecraft by the Canary tracking station indicated that pressure in the oxygen side of the cell was dropping steadily. The orbiting astronauts had also noticed the drop in pressure, and they told the Canary communicator: "We're a little bit concerned about this low pressure, but nothing beyond that."

Later during the second orbit, the astronauts ejected a radar evaluation pod, called REP for short, from the spacecraft. This was a small device equipped with radar components and flashing beacon lights. The Gemini 5 flight plan called for the spacecraft to change its orbit in order to draw away from the pod. Then, using the spacecraft's new radar system and his own piloting skill, Astronaut Cooper would attempt to move as close as 40 feet from the pod. Finally, he would steer the spacecraft slowly around the REP while Conrad took pictures of it.

Shortly after the REP left the spacecraft, however, Cooper, who had been giving careful attention to the ailing fuel cell, reported: "This gauge is falling . . . out the

A drawing of Gemini 5's Radar Evaluation Pod (superimposed on a Gemini 4 photo).

bottom and we decided that we were either going to have
to reënter pretty shortly . . . or power down."

At the Manned Spacecraft Center in Houston, Project
Gemini's flight director, Christopher Kraft, faced a difficult
decision. If he brought Gemini 5 down, the mission would
accomplish none of its objectives. On the other hand, the
safety of the two astronauts was of the utmost importance.
The spacecraft carried stand-by batteries to supply power
if the fuel cell failed completely, but their useful life was
limited to about nine hours.

During its sixth orbit the capsule would pass over a recovery area in the Pacific Ocean about 500 miles north-
east of Hawaii. Kraft ordered six Air Force planes deployed from Hickam Air Force Base in Hawaii, just in
case. Several surface vessels began heading that way as
well. Kraft advised the astronauts to use the bare minimum
of electrically powered equipment: their UHF (ultrahigh
frequency) receiver, two cooling pumps, one suit fan, and
a converter to change direct current to alternating current.
The astronauts would be orbiting the earth in what spacemen call "chimp mode." Like the chimpanzees who had
made flights in Mercury capsules, Cooper and Conrad
would be doing nothing to control their spaceship.

By the fifth orbit Gemini 5's future was beginning to
look a little brighter. Pressure in the oxygen side of the
fuel cell had fallen to 70 pounds per square inch; it had
been as high as 800 or 900 at the beginning of the flight.
But now it remained at 70 instead of dropping lower.
With the help of McDonnell Aircraft technicians, Mission
Control had analyzed the trouble as an inoperative heater

Mission officials at Houston Control discuss Gemini 5's fuel-cell problems. Flight Director Christopher Kraft is at center, with chin in hand.

in the liquid oxygen container. The heater wasn't warming the oxygen up fast enough to keep the fuel cell supplied.

When he learned that oxygen pressure was holding at 70, Kraft decided to keep Gemini 5 up for at least 18 orbits. A landing at the end of the eighteenth orbit would bring the astronauts down in the primary recovery zone in the western Atlantic, where a big recovery fleet waited to pick them up.

There was to be very little activity during the next day, however. Nonessential instruments would remain turned off, and there would still be no maneuvering of the spacecraft. Astronauts call this a "powered-down" condition.

The attempt to rendezvous with the REP had already been canceled. The pod had bobbed along within sight of the capsule for a while and then drifted away into space. But the astronauts hoped to complete most of the 17 other experiments assigned to Gemini 5. Many of them involved photography—of the moon, the stars, cloud formations, and certain features of the earth's surface.

By the afternoon of Gemini 5's second day in space, the flow of oxygen into the fuel cell had improved somewhat as the oxygen in the storage container gradually warmed up. Perhaps Gemini 5 would be able to complete a full eight days in space after all. In Houston Christopher Kraft announced: "Right now we are on the flight plan and we will probably be flying the next twelve to eighteen hours just as the flight plan says."

The flight plan kept the astronauts very busy. It kept them too busy, complained Gordon Cooper to James McDivitt, who was serving as the Manned Spacecraft Center's Mission

Communicator. Cooper continued: "You might have a little talk with the flight-planning people. They're filling us just a little bit too full. We can't get the equipment put together and torn apart in the time they're putting these things together."

And Charles Conrad, who had been taking pictures from the spacecraft, chimed in: "We've got to watch these lens changes. We've got every piece of gear in the spacecraft floating around in here. We can't keep up with it."

Soon, however, Conrad had time to compose a short song, which he sang to Houston: "Over the ocean, over the blue, here's Gemini Five singing to you."

During their thirty-second orbit, the busy astronauts started an experiment that the Manned Spacecraft Center had asked them to perform in place of the canceled rendezvous with the radar evaluation pod. The new experiment involved a rendezvous with an imaginary Agena rocket whose track had been calculated by a computer. Acting on information received from the ground, Gemini 5 would attempt to draw close to that track. A comparison of the imaginary rocket's track with the actual path of Gemini 5 would tell Mission Control how successful a real rendezvous attempt would have been.

The astronauts began the experiment by powering up their maneuvering equipment. Upon a command from the ground, they fired a rocket that changed the spacecraft's orbit to one that would bring them closer to the phantom Agena. About an hour later, in the thirty-third orbit, they fired a second and then a third rocket to move still closer. When the experiment was completed with one last maneuver in the thirty-fourth orbit, they had come within 17 miles of the Agena's plotted location. From there they could easily have "flown" to a real rocket.

That same day, Astronaut Cooper became the first space mechanic when he repaired a piece of optical equipment called a reticle. The reticle helps the pilot guide the space-craft by projecting an image on the windshield. The device was needed for a number of Gemini 5's observational ex-periments and it wasn't working.

Cooper later explained how he fixed the reticle with the help of a small screwdriver: "I took it all apart and com-pletely dismantled it and was installing the auxiliary line inside when I discovered that . . . when the cord was pulled out to the fairly full extent, it shorted out."

Having discovered what was wrong with the cord, Cooper quickly fixed it with some insulating tape. The ability to make in-flight repairs would be vital to the success of the long space flights of the future. Astronaut Cooper had an encouraging comment about that. "There is absolutely no problem," he said.

At 8:06 A.M. EST on Thursday, August 26, Gemini 5 established a new record for space travel by exceeding the old record set by Valery Bykovsky in the Soviet spaceship Vostok 5. But even as United States space officials were hailing the new record, bad news was coming from Gem-ini 5. One of its small maneuvering rockets had become stuck in the "open" position. This caused a small but steady loss of maneuvering fuel. The two rockets that turned the spacecraft to the left weren't working at all. And the fuel cell was causing concern once again.

This time the problem with the fuel cell involved the water that results from the combination of hydrogen and oxygen. It was planned that on Apollo flights the astronauts would drain off the water and drink it. But the fuel cell on Gemini 5 could not be drained, and the water remained in the cell's storage tank. Mission Control thought too much water might be accumulating in the tank. If that happened, the fuel cell would eventually drown in its own water. The only remedy was to cut down on the spacecraft's power consumption. Then the fuel cell would produce less water. The order went out to Gemini 5: "Power down again."

For the astronauts powering down, combined with their maneuvering difficulties, meant that they could no longer conduct experiments which required them to guide the spacecraft. Instead they began a period of drifting flight interrupted only by the few maneuvers necessary to control the capsule's tumbling motion.

With little to do except sleep and eat, the two astronauts listened to music piped to the spacecraft from the ground. They chatted with the ground controllers and occasionally received instructions. On one occasion they were told to do more exercising. To this Cooper replied: "OK, we thought we'd start taking long walks."

And Conrad joined in with: "We'll walk up and down the aisle of our big spacecraft."

More exercise might have helped the astronauts keep warm. After the power was cut, the spacecraft became very cold. Frost formed inside the cockpit and the astronauts' breath froze on the windshield. They turned up the temperatures in their pressure suits and Cooper reported: "I finally was freezing so bad . . . I broke out my wrist bands and put them on to stop the flow out of the suit."

The situation wasn't serious, however, and Gemini 5 continued to orbit the earth at 17,500 miles an hour. Although it might seem that the two astronauts were accomplishing very little by continuing to drift in the powered-down spacecraft, every orbit was adding to NASA's knowledge of what happens to men during long space flights. And experiments that required little or no fuel were continued.

During Gemini 5's 107th pass over the United States, a laser was directed skyward from the White Sands Proving Grounds in New Mexico. A laser is a beam of high-intensity light; NASA wanted to know if such a beam could be seen from space. The astronauts reported that they could see White Sands, but not the laser.

A few minutes later Cooper saw two of the twelve 2,000-foot by 2,000-foot squares of plowed and raked soil that had been arranged on a ranch near Laredo, Texas. White rectangles of Styrofoam-coated wallboard were laid out in each square in a north-south, east-west, or diagonal position to test the astronaut's ability to identify the direction of the rectangles. A similar "eye chart" was located 90 miles south of Carnarvon, Australia. There had been considerable controversy over just how well astronauts could see in space. Scientists hoped to settle the question with the help of the giant eye charts, but the Gemini 5 eye test was inconclusive.

Everyone agrees that Cooper and Conrad did see a Minuteman missile that was launched from Vandenberg

A *Gemini 5* photo of cloud formations over Cape Kennedy (looking south down the eastern Florida coastline).

Air Force Base as Gemini 5 crossed California during its forty-seventh orbit. The firing was timed to coincide with the arrival of the spacecraft and both men were watching for the missile. Conrad saw it first. He called out: "I see it, I see it. Hey, Gordo! Right through that hole in the clouds. There he goes."

Glistening in the sunlight, the Minuteman came within 200 miles of Gemini 5 as the astronauts took pictures and made infrared measurements of its exhaust plume. After reaching a height of 575 miles, the missile plunged down in the Pacific.

As the end of Gemini 5's journey approached, a tropical storm named Betsy moved up the Atlantic toward the primary landing area. Bad weather also threatened the secondary Atlantic landing area, creating another dilemma for Christopher Kraft. To land in the secondary area, Gemini 5 would have to come down one orbit short of a full eight days in space. However, that area had the more favorable forecast and the decision was made accordingly. After 120 orbits, Gemini 5 would come down 800 miles east of Jacksonville, Florida.

By the 118th orbit, the astronauts had finished their last experiments and begun stowing gear in preparation for landing. When they put their numerous pieces of equipment away, they were very careful not to change the spacecraft's center of gravity. Even a small change would affect its landing path. When Conrad reported that everything had been put away, the ground communicator remarked: "Now you're talking about a real accomplishment."

Gemini 5 completed its 120th revolution when it passed

over Cape Kennedy at 6:09 A.M. EST. (Revolution, a word often used interchangeably with orbit, is the official term for one trip around the earth beginning and ending over the same spot on earth.) The astronauts had already fired their four retro-rockets to slow the spacecraft and take it out of orbit.

Like Gemini 3 and Gemini 4 before it, Gemini 5 carried an on-board computer to help the astronauts make a very precise landing. When Astronaut Conrad read the data supplied by the computer, he realized at once that the spacecraft would hit the water short of its aiming point. He quickly sent out a message, but it was too late. Someone had put the wrong data into a computer at Houston. Information based on that data had been transmitted to the spacecraft's computer, which then guided Gemini 5 to a landing 103 miles short of the recovery ship *Lake Champlain*.

In spite of the landing error, rescue aircraft soon had the spacecraft in sight. They hovered over Gemini 5 until helicopters carrying pararescuemen arrived. The pararescuemen jumped into the water, placed a flotation collar around the capsule, and plugged a floating telephone into the spacecraft, which was still closed. One of the rescuemen then talked with the astronauts. When he finished, he gave his comrades the thumbs-up signal. Everything was all right inside the capsule.

Astronaut Cooper was the first to leave the spacecraft, followed by Conrad. They walked briskly around the flotation collar and got into a raft. Neither man showed any ill effects from his eight days in space. The astronauts confirmed this in the helicopter that carried them to the *Lake*

Gemini 5 astronauts arrive on the Lake Champlain *after eight days in space.*

Champlain. To the amazement of the helicopter crew, they did several deep knee bends.

Gemini 5's flight set ten space-flight records, notably that for the world's longest manned space flight: 190 hours and 56 minutes. Gemini 5 was not sent into space just to set records, however. Its primary objective was to test the effects of eight days in space on the two crewmen. Post-flight medical studies showed that Gordon Cooper and Charles Conrad passed the test with high marks. As one official at Mission Control put it: "We've now qualified one of the subsystems for the moon mission—that's the crew."

In spite of the problems that cropped up during its eight days in space, NASA considered Gemini 5 to be an almost complete success. The launching had been precisely on time, the rendezvous with the imaginary Agena rocket had been accurately carried out, and most of the other experiments assigned to Gemini 5 had been completed. As for the problems, the fuel-cell troubles that had marred the flight could be corrected, and so could the difficulty with the computer data.

Even as Christopher Kraft studied the results of Gemini 5, he was moving ahead with plans for Gemini 6. Using the experience gained during Gemini 5, Gemini 6 would attempt a rendezvous in space with a real, instead of an imaginary, Agena rocket.

CHAPTER 5
Project Gemini Loses a Rocket

September and October, 1965, were busy months at Cape Kennedy, the busiest the space center had ever known. On Pad 14 workers readied an Atlas intercontinental missile for launching. The Atlas had an Agena rocket for its second stage. Three miles to the north, on Pad 19, other workers swarmed around a Titan 2 booster and the spacecraft above it. The spacecraft was Gemini 6.

On Monday morning, October 25, Cape Kennedy was busier than ever. The workers had completed their tasks on the two launching pads and a complicated countdown was under way. For the first time, the United States was going to launch two big rockets in rapid succession. From Pad 14 the Atlas was scheduled to carry the Agena into orbit around the earth at 10 A.M. EST. Exactly one hour and 41 minutes later the Titan was to put Gemini 6 into orbit behind the Agena. Then the astronauts in Gemini 6, Walter M. Schirra, Jr., and Thomas P. Stafford, were to catch up with the Agena and dock with it.

Docking, or the joining of vehicles in space, had never been tried before. When astronauts returned from the moon, they would have to dock their lunar landing vehicle with the spaceship waiting to carry them back to earth. So experience in docking was one of the most important things NASA hoped to gain from Project Gemini.

Walter Schirra was Gemini 6's command pilot. On October 3, 1962, he had made a six-orbit flight as a Project Mercury astronaut. Pilot Thomas Stafford had never traveled in space before.

The two astronauts had trained for their flight for six months. Much of the training was in a special simulator that allowed them to practice rendezvous and docking procedures. When they entered their spacecraft on the morning of October 25, the astronauts were confident that they could successfully accomplish one of the most difficult assignments of the space age.

While they sat in Gemini 6 waiting for their space trip to begin, Command Pilot Schirra and Pilot Stafford worked on their checklists. They also followed the progress of the Atlas-Agena countdown. That launch came at exactly four seconds after 10 A.M., and a few minutes later the Atlas had lifted the Agena out of sight. The astronauts waited for word of a successful orbit for the Agena. Instead, they received this message: "We have lost telemetry [automatic radio signaling] from the Agena six minutes after its take-off. The telemetry loss was abrupt. We haven't given up, but it's an unhappy situation."

For 54 minutes Schirra and Stafford remained in their Gemini 6 capsule perched on top of the 90-foot-tall Titan.

Then, with the Agena still unreported, Gemini 6 was "scrubbed."

What had happened to the Agena? It was a very reliable rocket; it had only a few failures on its record and had been launched successfully some 185 times. It had carried television probes to the moon and one past the planet Mars. This time, however, the Agena had evidently blown up, soon after leaving the Atlas booster.

The untimely ending of the Gemini 6 mission disappointed space officials. They had hoped that Gemini 6 would accomplish the first successful docking. Because docking was so important, it would be tried on a later flight. Next to go, however, would be Gemini 7, already scheduled to be a 14-day space endurance mission in early December. And NASA quickly developed an even more exciting plan.

Three days later, on October 28, President Lyndon B. Johnson made a dramatic announcement. The United States planned to launch two manned spacecraft about ten days apart and the two pairs of astronauts would rendezvous in space!

One of the rendezvousing spacecraft would be Gemini 7, making its scheduled 14-day orbital journey. The other would be Gemini 6. According to the White House announcement, Gemini 7 was to be launched first. Then, about ten days later, Gemini 6 would go into orbit, locate Gemini 7, move in close to it, and fly in formation with the other spacecraft. The two spacecraft would not attempt to dock, however. The lost Agena had been equipped

Successful lift-off of Atlas-Agena on October 25, 1965. Minutes later the Agena target vehicle was lost.

with a shock-cushioned docking port, or notch, in its nose, but neither Gemini 6 nor 7 would have such a port.

Cape Kennedy had only one pad equipped to handle a Titan-Gemini launch. It was Pad 19, and NASA had never launched two successive manned space flights from it in less than 65 days. Could Gemini 7 and 6 be launched only ten days apart as the President had announced? With good weather and a little luck, space officials had told the President, they could do it. The intense heat of a rocket launch could scorch a launch pad, melt its metal fittings, and even crystallize its concrete, but the Titan booster usually did little damage to Pad 19. It took about 40,000 hours of work to ready a spacecraft-booster combination for launching, but the Gemini 6 spacecraft and booster were checked out and ready to go and so were Astronauts Schirra and Stafford. And preparations for Gemini 7 were well along.

Gemini 7 would have to be equipped with flashing strobe lights and a transponder for Gemini 6's radar to track. A transponder is an automatic answering radar device that sends signals when triggered by searching radar. A voice communications system between the two spacecraft would be necessary too. But these were minor additions.

By December 4 everything was ready for the dual space shot. The first astronauts to leave Pad 19 were Frank Borman and James A. Lovell, Jr., in Gemini 7. Neither man had traveled in space before, but like all astronauts they had trained hard for their journey. In addition, they had undergone an unusually large number of medical tests because they were scheduled to remain in space for 14 days. This was six days longer than Gemini 5 Astronauts Cooper and Conrad had stayed there. Dr. Berry and his staff were anxious to learn what effect, if any, the extra six days would have on the astronauts' health.

One of the tests involved the loss of calcium and nitrogen from the body during space flight. For several days before the launching, Astronauts Borman and Lovell ate a controlled diet. They also bathed in distilled water. The water was then analyzed for any traces of calcium and nitrogen that washed off in their perspiration. After the 14-day space journey the two astronauts were to take another distilled-water bath. That water would be analyzed and the results compared with those obtained before the flight. The astronauts' long underwear was to be washed in distilled water also. By this procedure, space medical men hoped to discover if the sweat glands disposed of calcium and nitrogen during long periods of weightlessness.

Gemini 7 got off to a very good start. The launch, scheduled for 2:30 P.M. EST on December 4, was only three seconds late. Six minutes after lift-off, Gemini 7 was in orbit around the earth. Handling his craft like a veteran spaceman, Command Pilot Frank Borman turned it around as soon as the Titan's second stage separated from the capsule. He adjusted his speed to that of the Titan, then flew close to the Titan for 17 minutes. Astronauts call this maneuver "station keeping." If Borman had first approached the Titan from a considerable distance, he would have been rendezvousing with the Titan.

The two astronauts were wearing new, lightweight space-suits. Although the suit could be pressurized, neither Borman's nor Lovell's was. (The spacecraft's cabin was pres-

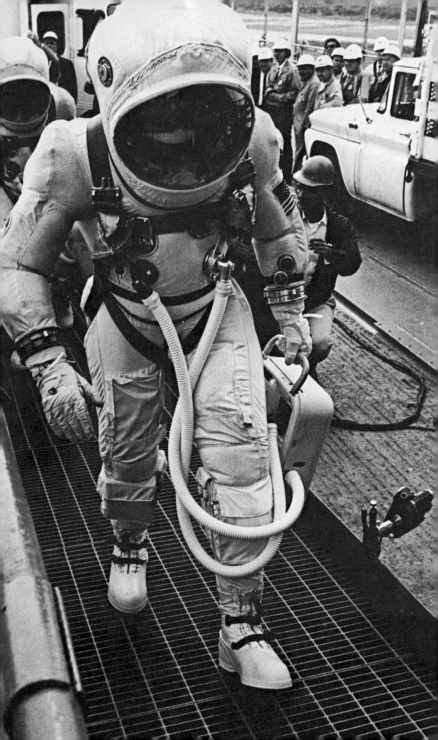

surized, of course.) The new suit was designed for comfort. Its hood was much larger than the old helmet, but it could be unzipped and folded back during an ordinary space flight. Underneath it the astronauts wore regular flight helmets. Unlike earlier spacesuits, this one could be taken off and stored during flight; and the men planned to remove their suits later in the mission.

Like Gemini 5, Gemini 7 carried a fuel-cell system, and like the one on Gemini 5, it caused concern early in the flight. But the problem was solved after a conference between John Yardley, a trouble-shooter for the McDonnell Aircraft Corporation, and experts at Mission Control in Houston. On the basis of data sent automatically by the spacecraft, they decided that the trouble was in an indicator light on the capsule's control panel and not in the fuel-cell system. The astronauts were told to ignore the warning light; they could even put a piece of tape over it if they wanted to. But Borman and Lovell decided that the light didn't bother them that much.

A little less than four hours after their takeoff, the astronauts began a series of course corrections that would place them near Gemini 6 several days later. Their first adjustment raised Gemini 7's minimum altitude, or perigee, from 100 to 138 miles. It was accomplished by a technique that astronauts call "burning on stars." The ground controllers gave Borman and Lovell a star to aim at—in this case, the bright star Spica. Then they told the astronauts to burn, or fire, the OAMS thrusters for one minute and 11 seconds to climb into the new orbit.

Wearing their new lightweight spacesuits, Gemini 7 astronauts march up the ramp to the Pad 19 elevator.

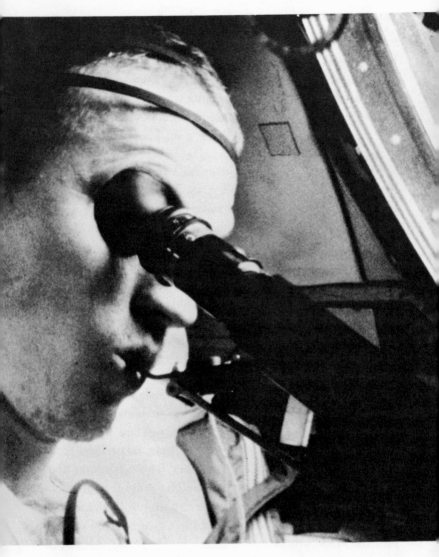

Sitting suitless in Gemini 7, Astronaut Borman carries out an optical experiment.

When Gemini 7 passed over Texas, the two astronauts were supposed to look for the "eye chart" spread out on the field near Laredo. At first visibility was poor and Borman and Lovell had trouble identifying the rectangular markings that had been placed on the huge plowed squares. During later orbits, however, their record improved.

Another early experiment that failed was an attempt to send a message to earth on a laser beam. After a laser transmitting station at the White Sands Missile Range locked in on the spacecraft, the astronauts used a laser-emitting device to send a voice message back to the station. But no message was ever received.

One experiment was very successful. During the third day in space, Astronaut James Lovell took off his spacesuit and became the first United States spaceman to travel without such protection. It took the astronaut more than 20 minutes to remove his suit because he had to be very careful not to disturb any of its wiring.

Lovell said later that at first he felt rather cold sitting in Gemini 7 in nothing more than his long underwear, but after a couple of hours he became quite comfortable. And after a day or so without his suit, he no longer worried that the pressure in the capsule might drop suddenly. If that had happened, Astronaut Borman, who still wore a suit, would have helped Lovell get back into his as quickly as possible.

In spite of the possibility that a capsule might suddenly depressurize in space, the experiment convinced Lovell that, in the future, astronauts on long missions would remove their suits. When Astronaut Borman also removed his suit later in the flight, he agreed with his copilot.

Because they were going to spend 14 days in a very small capsule, the two astronauts had to be very careful about their housekeeping. If they didn't they would soon be smothered by used equipment, empty food packages, and other debris. Before the flight, they searched the spacecraft to locate even the smallest crevice where something could be stored. And before they went to sleep each "night," they made sure that their capsule was in order.

Unlike the astronauts on earlier Gemini missions, Borman and Lovell were scheduled to sleep at the same time. The other astronauts had complained that when one man tried to sleep, the activities of his companion would wake him up.

The Gemini 7 astronauts set their watches on Houston time and observed a regular work day. They had breakfast, lunch, and dinner, and at "night" they "went to bed." They had no beds, of course, and it was seldom night for Gemini 7 in space when it was night in Houston. They covered the spacecraft windows to make it dark inside and relaxed on their contour couches as best they could. Furthermore, there were no communications from the ground to wake them up during their sleeping period. Astronaut Lovell was the better sleeper of the two, but neither man missed as much sleep as the earlier astronauts had.

While Frank Borman and Jim Lovell traveled around the earth conducting experiments, eating, and sleeping, things were happening fast at Cape Kennedy. In fact, a small army of technicians began to examine and repair Pad 19 almost as soon as Gemini 7 left it. Fortunately the

Less than 24 hours after the Gemini 7 lift-off, Gemini 6 is hoisted into place.

pad had suffered very little damage. Forty-five minutes after the Gemini 7 lift-off, the first stage of the Titan booster for Gemini 6 was on its way from a hanger to Pad 19. The Gemini 6 launch was scheduled for December 13, only nine days away.

CHAPTER 6
A Rendezvous in Space

As it turned out, it was only December 12 when Astronauts Walter Schirra and Tom Stafford climbed back into Gemini 6 for their postponed trip into space. Gemini officials and technicians, who once needed at least 65 days to prepare for a flight, had finished their task in only eight days. But a very difficult launching still lay ahead. In order to rendezvous with Gemini 7 as planned, Gemini 6 had to leave Pad 19 precisely on schedule at 9:54 A.M. For every 100 seconds delay in the launching, Gemini 6 would have to wait for Gemini 7 to complete one more orbit of the earth.

The clock stood at just six seconds after 9:54 when the two main engines of the Titan ignited. The usual cloud of rust-colored smoke covered Pad 19 as observers waited for the rocket to rise. Inside the spaceship Schirra and Stafford were waiting for the lift-off, too. Each man gripped the ring that would eject him from the capsule in case of trouble during the launching.

The lift-off clock on Gemini 6's instrument panel began to tick off the seconds, the signal that lift-off had begun. But had Gemini 6 left the launching pad? The astronauts could feel no movement. And the instrument panel's red engine lights were still on. They were supposed to burn until the Titan had developed enough power for lift-off. Which instrument, if any, should the men trust?

The two astronauts had only a second to assess the situation and decide what to do. Should they pull the rings, eject themselves from the capsule, and get safely away from the malfunctioning Titan? Or should they stay where they were?

Schirra and Stafford decided to stay. They knew that the Titan's hydrazine fuel would burn but not explode. And in spite of the lift-off clock, the men had not felt the Titan leave Pad 19. It was a quickly made decision, but it turned out to be the right one. If the astronauts had ejected themselves from the spacecraft, it would have needed major repairs before it could fly again. Or Gemini 6 might have been canceled for good. Instead, the mission was rescheduled for three days later.

One hundred and eighty-five miles above Cape Kennedy, Astronauts Borman and Lovell had watched the activity

Launch exhaust smoke drifts from Pad 19 after

Gemini 6 fails to lift off on December 12, 1965.

on Pad 19 with the aid of a small telescope. When Mission Control told them Gemini 6 had been scrubbed, Borman replied: "We saw it light up; we saw it shut down."

Gemini 6 was the first launch abort in the Gemini manned space-flight program. Just what had happened? Technicians soon discovered the answer. An electrical plug had fallen out of the rocket's tail before lift-off, rather than immediately after. When the plug fell out, it delivered a false lift-off signal to the lift-off clock in the capsule. The false signal also went to an automatic sequencing device at the Cape Kennedy Launch Control Center. Because things were not happening in the proper order, the automatic sequencer shut down the Titan's engines.

But the technicians discovered something far more serious than a loose plug when they examined the engines. A worker had left a dime-sized plastic dust cover in the Titan's "plumbing" system. Even if the plug had not fallen out too soon, the dust cover would have caused the engines to shut down in another second or so. Moreover, the dust cover had been in the Titan on October 25, the day Gemini 6 was to have rendezvoused with the Agena rocket. Gemini 6 would not have flown that day either.

Astronauts Schirra and Stafford climbed into the trouble-plagued Gemini 6 for the third time on December 15. The Titan booster had been inspected thoroughly. It was ready to go and so were the astronauts.

Once again Gemini 7 was 185 miles above Cape Kennedy at launch time, 8:37 A.M. Because of clouds over the Cape, Astronauts Borman and Lovell didn't see Gemini 6, but they saw the contrails (condensation trails) that marked its upward path. Borman and Lovell were feeling tired and cramped after 11 days in space, but they had encountered no serious problems during their long flight. Now they looked forward to rendezvousing with their fellow astronauts.

Before a rendezvous could take place, Gemini 6 had to catch up with Gemini 7. Gemini 6's orbit ranged from 100 to 165 miles above the earth's surface, while Gemini 7's altitude was 185 miles. In addition, Gemini 7 was about 1,200 miles ahead of Gemini 6. However, the speed of orbiting objects is dependent on their altitude. A spaceship in a low orbit has to travel faster in order to keep from being pulled back to earth by gravity. Therefore, as soon as it went into orbit, Gemini 6 began to catch up with Gemini 7.

But Astronauts Schirra and Stafford had to gradually raise Gemini 6's orbit or they would continue to speed around the earth underneath Gemini 7. They raised the orbit in a series of carefully planned maneuvers.

At the end of Gemini 6's first orbit, Astronaut Schirra fired his thrusters to raise the high point, or apogee, of the next orbit from 165 to 169 miles. Then, with another burst from the thrusters, he raised the orbit's perigee from 100 to 139 miles. During these maneuvers Gemini 6 continued to gain on Gemini 7 because it was still in a lower orbit. When only 439 miles separated the two spacecraft, Schirra moved Gemini 6 into an orbit that crossed the equator at the same angle that Gemini 7 crossed at: 28.9 degrees.

All of Schirra's moves were carefully worked out in advance on the computers at the Manned Spacecraft Center.

The first rendezvous in space of two manned capsules: looking at Gemini 7 through the hatch window of Gemini 6.

When the two ships were 115 miles apart, Gemini 6's radar locked on to Gemini 7's and helped guide Schirra. Information supplied by Tom Stafford from the on-board computer also helped guide the spacecraft. Schirra executed all the maneuvers perfectly. The skillful space pilot saw Gemini 7 for the first time after he had raised Gemini 6's orbit to about 170 miles and moved to within 50 miles of the other spacecraft.

With an assist from its thrusters, Gemini 6 passed under Gemini 7 and then climbed up through 7's flight path. Once ahead and slightly above the "friendly target," as Borman and Lovell called themselves, Schirra fired thrusters to brake his movement. He had been flying backward, so Gemini 6's nose was pointed toward Gemini 7's nose as the two spaceships approached one another.

The tracking ship *Coastal Sentry Quebec* (CSQ) in the Pacific below the two Geminis was receiving Gemini 6's range reports and relaying them to Mission Control at Houston and to a nationwide TV and radio audience. Astronaut Stafford reported: "One point seven miles; one point three miles; one mile." And finally: "We're at a hundred and twenty feet and sitting."

A loud cheer went up at Mission Control. But Astronaut Schirra hadn't finished. As the two spaceships whizzed around the earth at 17,500 miles an hour, he edged closer to Gemini 7—moving to within 20 feet, then 10, and then 6. Later he edged up to within a foot of the other spacecraft.

It was a remarkable achievement—a true rendezvous in space. In 1962 the Soviet spaceships Vostok 3 and Vostok 4 had passed within three miles of each other. But Gemini 6 had sought out Gemini 7, moved up very close, and stayed by it.

Later, in describing his approach to Gemini 7, Astronaut Schirra said: "The sunlight on Seven was absolutely the brightest thing I have ever seen in my life. My eyes hurt. It was a klieg-like carbon arc lamp completely saturating my eyeballs."

After flying awhile in a nose-to-nose formation, Gemini 6 began to move around Gemini 7 while the two pairs of astronauts took pictures. They observed that the heat generated when the spacecraft went into orbit had scorched the paint of the United States flags that decorated the capsules. Gemini 6 also noticed that Gemini 7 was trailing some straps from its adapter section and radioed: "You guys are really a shaggy-looking group with all those wires hanging out."

Gemini 7 replied that Gemini 6 had some too. The straps were the remains of the insulating material that once covered the explosive charges that had separated the Geminis from their Titan boosters.

The astronauts found that they could see each other quite well. Earlier, Mission Control had directed both Borman and Lovell to remove their space suits, but they had put them on again for the rendezvous. They had not been able to shave, however. This led Astronaut Lovell in Gemini 7 to ask Astronaut Schirra in Gemini 6: "Can you see Frank's beard, Wally?"

Schirra answered: "I can see yours better right now." Then he said to Lovell: "Looks like you just wiped your mouth, Jim. Did you?"

Lovell admitted that he had.

When Schirra asked how the food supply was holding out, the veteran space travelers in Gemini 7 answered: "Oh, we're in good shape. It's holding out, but it's the same thing day after day."

After six hours of formation flying, the spaceships separated. Gemini 6 moved into an orbit that placed it at some distance from Gemini 7. The maneuver officially ended the rendezvous, although the two Geminis were still within sight of one another.

All four astronauts were tired. After the spaceships separated, the men went to sleep. Two days of space flight still lay ahead of Borman and Lovell. Schirra and Stafford were scheduled to land the next morning.

After 25 hours and 51 minutes in space, Gemini 6 splashed down into the Atlantic Ocean at 10:29 A.M. EST. It landed only 13 miles from the carrier *Wasp*. Because they were so close to the *Wasp*, the astronauts decided not to leave the capsule. Instead, they remained inside the spaceship until it had been hoisted to the deck of the *Wasp*.

Meanwhile, Astronauts Borman and Lovell continued their journey in Gemini 7. They had hoped to see the firing of Gemini 6's retro-rockets, but they couldn't turn their spacecraft to get in the right viewing position. The thrusters needed for that maneuver were no longer working. So they used their radio to send a good-bye message to their departing space companions and watched them move out of sight.

Borman and Lovell settled down to another day of work in space. It was a day filled with tension, however, because

Astronauts Stafford (left) and Schirra climb out of their capsule onto the deck of the Wasp.

they were worried about the fuel-cell system again. By afternoon Borman was reporting: "Looks to me like this time the fuel cells are really on their way."

Power output from the fuel-cell system had dropped noticeably. Apparently one of the two fuel-cell sections had flooded. Both the astronauts in Gemini 7 and the flight directors on the ground kept a careful check on the system for the rest of the day. If the situation didn't improve, Gemini 7 would have to come down early.

Because the two astronauts had been in space so long, their postflight physical examinations would be extremely important. The carrier *Wasp* in the Dash 1 area—the primary Atlantic recovery area—was the only ship equipped to give the thorough postflight examinations planned for them. If they had to land in one of the secondary recovery areas, no such facilities would be available. Moreover, in a secondary recovery area they might have to wait several hours in the capsule before being picked up. If that happened and they became ill, would it be from the motion of the capsule bobbing in the water? Or would they be suffering from the aftereffects of their space journey? It would be very difficult to tell.

Astronaut Borman knew where he wanted to land. After discussing the problem with Christopher Kraft at Mission Control, he said: "I'd like to land somewhere near the carrier."

And Kraft assured him: "I'm going to be as certain that the fuel cell is going to last when we go by Dash One area tomorrow as I absolutely can."

After hours of anxious monitoring, Mission Control decided that the fuel-cell problem had been corrected. When the astronauts awakened early the next morning, they received a message from Houston: "The blue team is happy to give you the GO for the big 207-1." That meant that Gemini 7 would come down at the beginning of its 207th revolution after a full 14 days in space, and it would land in the primary Atlantic recovery area.

During their fourteenth and final day in space, Astronauts Borman and Lovell used up what was left of their film and conducted some last experiments. And like all Gemini astronauts, they prepared for landing by making sure that every piece of gear in the spacecraft was properly stowed away.

Gemini 7 settled down into the Atlantic Ocean at 9:05 A.M. EST on December 18. And it landed only eight miles from the *Wasp*—the closest of all the Gemini landings. A few minutes later the two astronauts emerged from the spacecraft. They were bearded, stiff, and tired, but they were beaming.

One of the helicopters from the *Wasp* picked up the astronauts and carried them to the recovery ship, where a band played "Anchors Aweigh" and hundreds of sailors cheered their arrival. Although they complained that their legs felt heavy, Borman and Lovell jumped from the helicopter to the deck with no signs of giddiness or faintness. And their medical tests indicated that they had suffered no serious effects from their $330\frac{1}{2}$ hours in space. There were no lasting changes in the astronauts' pulse rates or blood pressures. Muscles which were weak when they landed soon regained their former strength. Both Borman and Lovell lost some calcium and other minerals, but the loss was a small one.

The long flight of Gemini 7 established several new endurance records. And, with the flight of Gemini 6, it answered some important questions about space travel. Astronauts Frank Borman and James Lovell proved beyond a doubt that it was possible to remain away from earth for 14 days. During that time they had breathed pure oxygen, eaten dehydrated foods, and lived in a capsule scarcely larger than a phone booth. Furthermore, they had used a fuel-cell system for 14 days, albeit with some problems. Fuel cells would be a necessity on long space voyages.

Astronaut Lovell is hoisted up to the recovery helicopter after the Gemini 7 splashdown.

Astronaut Walter Schirra's skillful piloting of Gemini 6 was a convincing demonstration that one orbiting spacecraft could rendezvous with another.

Although there was still work to be done, the goal of an American landing on the moon had moved closer to realization.

CHAPTER 7
A Short Circuit in Space

In one short year, Project Gemini astronauts had tried out a new spacecraft and traveled in it for 8 and, later, 14 days. They had successfully carried out extravehicular activity and a rendezvous in space. But they had not yet docked a Gemini spacecraft with another orbiting vehicle. That important mission was assigned to Gemini 8, scheduled for March, 1966.

Neil Armstrong and David Scott were the astronauts chosen for Gemini 8. Neither had flown in space before, but Neil Armstrong, the command pilot of Gemini 8, had flown in near-space. Before becoming an astronaut, Armstrong flew an experimental rocket plane called the X-15. The X-15 program, jointly sponsored by NASA and the Air

Force, was designed to obtain information on the problems of airplane flight at high speeds and high altitudes. Armstrong flew an X-15 to a height of 207,500 feet— almost 40 miles. On another X-15 flight he reached a speed of 3,989 miles an hour. Commercial jets usually reach an altitude of 25,000 or 35,000 feet, and the record speed for a commercial jet is 638.8 miles an hour; in comparison, Armstrong flew very high and fast indeed.

Gemini 8 was scheduled to remain in space for three days. During that time the two astronauts had a variety of tasks to perform. After docking with an Agena rocket, they were going to maneuver the Gemini-Agena combination. Its total weight of more than $7\frac{1}{2}$ tons would make it the heaviest manned space vehicle ever to orbit the earth.

During Gemini 8's second day in space, Astronaut Scott was scheduled to leave the spacecraft for $2\frac{1}{2}$ hours. In addition to examining the Gemini-Agena combination, he was to remove the film left on Gemini 8's windows by the smoke and gases of launching. And he planned to tidy up any wires that might be hanging from the spacecraft's adapter section.

Another of Scott's extravehicular activities required him to remove a power wrench and an ordinary hand wrench from a special kit that Gemini 8 carried near its adapter section. He was to try them both on a bolt that was hooked electrically to a gauge that would measure the amount of turning force he applied. Scott was also going to use the power wrench to remove and replace a metal plate on the tool kit. Information gained from his experi-

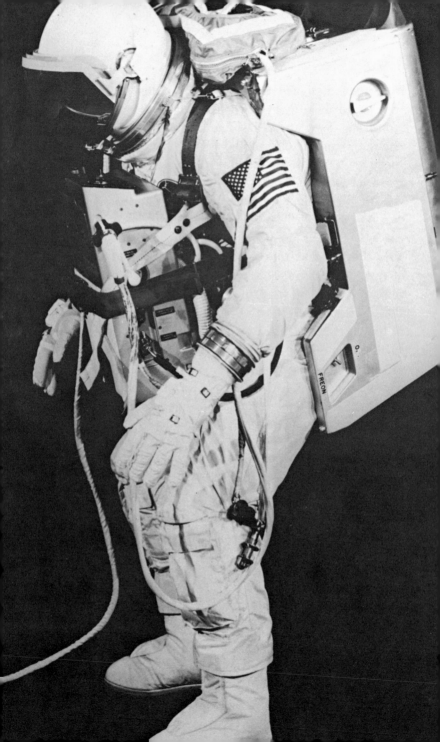

ment with the wrenches would help engineers design tools that were easy to use in space.

When Gemini 8 approached the dark side of the earth, Scott was to climb into the adapter section. While waiting for the 45-minute "night" to end, he would don a 92-pound extravehicular support pack (ESP). He would need the ESP, with its 79-minute oxygen supply and its extra fuel for his hand-held propulsion gun, for his next maneuvers.

At daylight, Armstrong would separate Gemini 8 from the Agena. Scott was then to emerge from the adapter. Using a 75-foot extension to his regular oxygen-supplying umbilical cord, or tether, he would then "fly formation" with Gemini 8 and the Agena. After performing some additional extravehicular chores, Scott was to remove and discard the ESP and the 75-foot tether. Then he was to climb back into Gemini 8.

Before ending their flight, the astronauts were to practice more rendezvous and docking maneuvers with the Agena; and they had a number of experiments to perform.

With such an ambitious mission planned for Gemini 8, space officials were understandably dismayed when technicians discovered a leak in the Atlas rocket that was to boost the Agena docking target into orbit. They found the leak just before the final countdown was to begin. And at almost the same time, spacecraft technicians found a leak in Gemini 8. It was in the water system that cooled the astronauts' suits.

Gear for David Scott's space walk, including both chest and back life-support packs.

The last-minute leaks caused Gemini 8 to be postponed for 24 hours. While technicians worked on the Atlas and the capsule, Astronauts Armstrong and Scott reviewed their flight plans and practiced rendezvous and docking procedures in a simulator. The success of Gemini 8 would depend largely on the skill with which they accomplished those maneuvers.

Twenty-four hours later both the Atlas and the capsule had been repaired. The Atlas was scheduled to leave Cape Kennedy's Pad 14 at 10 A.M. on March 16. Gemini 8 was to follow from Pad 19 at 11:41 A.M. If Gemini 8 was more than 4 minutes and 7 seconds late, its launching would have to be postponed until March 18. There would not be another good "launch window" open until then.

A launch window is the period during which a space-craft can be launched into orbit close enough to a second orbiting spacecraft to make rendezvous possible. The opening and closing of the March 16 launch window depended on the speed and altitude of the Agena, the speed of the earth's rotation, the precise time of Gemini 8's launching, and the speed of the Titan as it boosted the spaceship into orbit. The problem of getting Gemini 8 into the proper position behind the Agena has been compared to a man on a merry-go-round trying to throw a forward pass to a man on an adjacent merry-go-round that is revolving at a different speed.

The launching sequence began successfully when the Atlas lifted the Agena into orbit on schedule at 10:00 A.M.

"It looks like we've got a live one up there for you," Mission Control told the astronauts, who were waiting in the Gemini capsule for their own launching.

"Roger! That's just what the doctor ordered," Scott answered.

When Gemini 8 followed the Agena into orbit, at 11:41, the launch window was wide open. Mission Control informed the two astronauts: "You're looking good, Eight."

Armstrong agreed: "We're looking good up here." Referring to the ignition of the Titan's second stage, he added: "We saw the fireball out there."

Then Mission Control asked if the astronauts like space travel, and they answered: "You bet! It's all right."

Astronauts Armstrong and Scott were not the only space travelers that day. The Soviet cosmodogs Veterok (Breezy) and Ugolok (Coal Lump) had been orbiting the earth since February 22. Their spacecraft had a very high orbit —from 116 to 562 miles above the earth. As a result, they traveled through part of the lower Van Allen belt.

Both the Soviet Union and the United States were concerned about the intense radiation that had been discovered in two belts that surround most of the earth. The radiation belts were named for the American physicist, Dr. James A. Van Allen. He was responsible for the instruments that detected the radiation when sent into space in January, 1958.

When Veterok and Ugolok ended their flight later on March 16, Soviet space officials announced that they were in good condition. The dogs had evidently suffered no immediate effects from their travels in the lower Van Allen belt.

Astronauts Armstrong and Scott were orbiting the earth

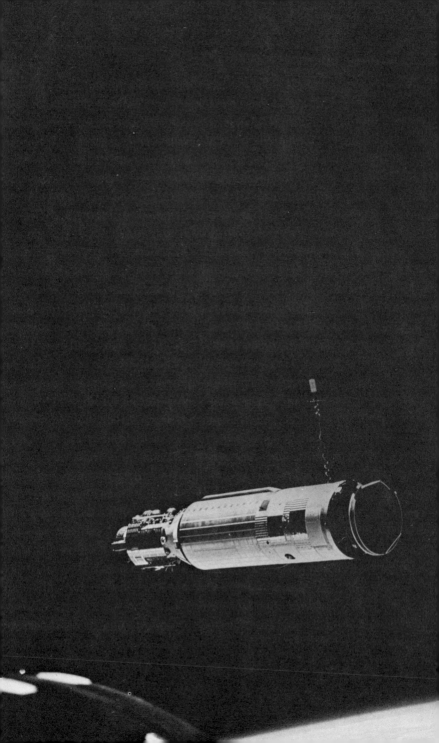

in Gemini 8 at an altitude that varied from 99 to 168 miles. Their Agena target was traveling in a 185-mile-high circular orbit, similar to the one Gemini 7 had flown. Gemini 8 Command Pilot Armstrong used the same maneuvers that Gemini 6 Command Pilot Walter Schirra, Jr., had used when he caught up with Gemini 7. And Armstrong was equally successful. His copilot sent a pleased report back to Houston. "We've got a real winner here," he said.

Gemini 8 was flying in darkness when it approached the 26-foot Agena, but the two astronauts saw the Agena's lights. They followed them into the sunrise and caught up with the Agena over the Western Pacific.

"It's pretty bright up here," Scott remarked when the Agena and Gemini 8 moved into the sunlight.

As the two spacecraft crossed the Pacific Ocean, Armstrong and Scott edged closer to the Agena. Finally Armstrong reported: "We are a hundred and fifty feet apart and station keeping. The Agena looks fine. The antennas are all in the proper position." A moment later Armstrong reported that he was within 80 feet of the Agena.

At the beginning of its fifth orbit, Gemini 8 flew over the tracking ship *Rose Knot Victor,* stationed in the Atlantic off the coast of Brazil. The *Rose Knot* relayed an order to Gemini 8 from Mission Control in Houston: "Proceed with the docking."

The astronauts were already in radar contact with the unmanned Agena. They had sent it a message to loosen its docking collar—a cone 58 inches in diameter. They

The Agena target vehicle, about 35 feet from Gemini 8.

sent another signal which turned on two approach lights near the docking cone.

As Gemini 8 drew close to the Agena, the astronauts pushed a switch that extended a guide bar on the capsule's nose. Then, using their maneuvering thrusters, they nudged Gemini 8's nose into the Agena until the guide bar slid into a slot in the docking cone. Astronaut Armstrong reapplied his thrusters to obtain a slight forward movement, three spring-loaded mooring latches gripped Gemini 8's nose, and the docking collar stiffened. Gemini 8 was docked with the Agena!

Pleased officials at Mission Control in Houston relayed their congratulations to the Gemini 8 astronauts. Armstrong in turn described the docking: "It was very stable. There was little oscillation. . . . A real smoothy."

Following his flight plan carefully, Armstrong shut down the power in Gemini 8 and began to use the Agena's thrusters to control the combined craft. By sending a sequence of 15 commands to the Agena's control system, Astronaut Scott turned the Gemini-Agena around so that Gemini 8 traveled with its blunt end forward. Then Scott sent another command to the Agena. This time he directed it to turn on its tape recorder. The recorder would note all future movements of the Agena.

Just as Scott finished his command to the Agena, the two linked spacecraft began a pronounced rolling and slewing movement. Thinking the unwanted motion was coming from the Agena, Armstrong switched off the Agena's power and tried to stabilize the combined spacecraft with Gemini 8's thrusters. The motion increased. And

Looking down Gemini 8's nose at the Agena, a moment before docking.

when he turned off Gemini 8's thrusters, the rolling and slewing became so violent he knew he could not separate Gemini 8 from the Agena. But unless they were separated, and soon, the two spacecraft might break up.

Armstrong continued his methodical search for a solution to the problem. In case the Agena's power had not switched off, he sent a second "shut down" command to the Agena. Then using Gemini 8's thrusters again, he managed to stabilize the combined spacecraft enough to disengage Gemini 8 from the Agena. Part of the astronauts' problem was solved. Gemini 8 was undocked, but it was tumbling out of control.

Cheers for the perfect docking had hardly died away at Mission Control when a disturbing message came from the tracking ship *Coastal Sentry Quebec*, on station in the Pacific off the coast of China. CSQ was picking up radar signals that indicated Gemini 8 and the Agena had separated.

Then Gemini 8 moved within radio range of CSQ and Astronaut Armstrong confirmed their fears. "We consider this problem serious. We're tumbling end over end, but we are disengaged from the Agena."

The tracking ship's startled communicator asked what the problem was and Armstrong answered: "It's a roll and we can't seem to turn anything off." He added that his orbital-attitude-and-maneuvering-system pressure was down to zero. That meant that Gemini 8's regular control system was no longer operating.

In the emergency, Armstrong turned to Gemini 8's re-ëntry control system (RCS). Its main purpose was to guide the spacecraft during the reëntry phase of its mission. Now it was the astronauts' only means of stabilizing the wildly tumbling spacecraft. But when Armstrong tried to activate the RCS, it wouldn't work either. He told the *Coastal Sentry:* "We're in a violent left roll at the present time. Our RCS is armed but we can't fire it." Before the reëntry control system could be used, small explosive valve-openers called "squibs" had to be detonated. However, when Armstrong initiated the firing process, nothing happened.

His next message was more encouraging: "We are regaining control of the spacecraft slowly in RCS direct." The reëntry control system had begun to function and, with its thrusters, Armstrong was slowly bringing Gemini 8's motion under control.

By using the reëntry control system the astronauts had ended the Gemini 8 mission. Safety rules required that an orbiting spacecraft come down promptly once that system was activated. However, Gemini 8 would not be able to land in the primary Atlantic recovery area. To do so would mean either a risky nighttime landing or an equally risky extension of its flight until the next day.

John Hodge, Gemini 8's flight director at the Manned Spacecraft Center, had to decide when and where the spacecraft should come down. Although the Manned Spacecraft Center was not in direct contact with Gemini 8, the *Coastal Sentry* had kept Hodge informed of the developing emergency.

When the troubled Gemini 8 made contact with the tracking station in Hawaii, the flight director's preliminary instructions were ready for the astronauts: "Be advised we're planning to come into a Dash Three area. We're looking into six- or seven-three at this time."

The message told the astronauts that they would be landing during the sixth or seventh revolution in the Dash 3 landing zone—in the Pacific off the coast of China.

Hawaii also told the astronauts to turn their spacecraft around so that its blunt end would be forward and ready for reëntry. By this time Gemini 8 was under control and in drifting flight.

Flight Director Hodge decided to wait until the seventh orbit to bring Gemini 8 down. This would give the astronauts time to prepare their spacecraft for reëntry. It would also enable the recovery force in the Western Pacific to move toward the splashdown area. Since this was a secondary area, the recovery force was a small one—the destroyer *Mason* and some Air Force rescue planes based in Okinawa.

Like its flight, Gemini 8's reëntry was full of suspense. The countdown that preceded the firing of the retro-rockets had to be relayed from the Manned Spacecraft Center to the tracking station at Kano, Nigeria, and from Kano to Gemini 8. But when the count reached "two," the spacecraft lost contact with Kano. Undaunted, the astronauts finished the count and fired the retro-rockets to start Gemini 8 on its downward journey.

During the entire reëntry, for 30 long minutes, Gemini 8 was out of contact with the ground. The tracking network waited anxiously as the capsule streaked down across Saudi Arabia, northern India, and central China toward its

Appearing cheerful after their harrowing ride, Astronauts Scott (left) and Armstrong wait for the recovery ship.

Pacific landing area.

The first word of Gemini 8's fate came from one of the rescue planes. Gemini 8 had been spotted, descending under its huge parachute, just seven miles from its intended landing point. Air Force pararescuemen were in the water almost as soon as the spacecraft landed. They fixed a bright yellow flotation collar on the capsule and reported that the astronauts were alive and well.

Neil Armstrong and David Scott were indeed alive and well, and they appeared undisturbed by their harrowing ordeal. While they waited for the *Mason* to pick them up, they opened the capsule's hatch doors and ate a leisurely lunch in the sun.

A busy time lay ahead for the astronauts, however. Before sending up another docking mission, space-agency officials wanted to find out what caused the strange things that happened to Gemini 8. The first-hand accounts of the astronauts would supply important information. So would instrumentation records from the Gemini 8 spacecraft and the Agena.

After all of the available evidence had been studied, Robert R. Gilruth, the director of the Manned Spacecraft Center, announced that Gemini 8 had been thrown into its violent tumbling when a short circuit caused one of its rocket thrusters to fire. The astronauts could neither hear nor see the thruster firing, so they were unable to take corrective action.

To prevent a similar occurrence in the future, the Gemini capsule's wiring was rearranged and a special check on the thruster control system was added to the countdown.

Meanwhile, the Agena target vehicle, unaffected by Gemini 8's difficulties, continued to orbit the earth. Flight controllers at the Manned Spacecraft Center moved the Agena into a 250-mile-high circular orbit and "parked" it there by remote control. Later it would serve as the target for another Gemini docking mission.

Neil Armstrong and David Scott received the highest

praise for their cool handling of the Gemini 8 emergency. The astronauts agreed that their test-pilot experience had helped them in their struggle to control the spacecraft when it was tumbling as fast as one revolution per second. In describing that part of the flight, Armstrong said that they felt some "anxiety," but they never for a moment doubted that they would return to earth.

In spite of their wild ride in Gemini 8, the astronauts were enthusiastic about traveling in space. "The sights and sounds of space flight," Command Pilot Armstrong declared, "are unparalleled here on earth. Seeing your own thrusters fire, the reflection from the window . . . watching fires on the ground in Africa, seeing storms from above . . . and observing the whole weather panorama from a hundred and fifteen miles or more above the earth is something that unfortunately can't really be described adequately."

CHAPTER 8
An Angry Alligator
and a Fogged Visor

Preparations for a Project Gemini mission begin several months before the actual flight. First, space-agency planners decide what they want the space flight to accomplish. Then they select a team of astronauts and a backup team and work out a training program for them. While the astronauts train, technicians prepare a Titan 2 booster and a Gemini capsule for their space trip. For missions that involve docking, technicians also prepare an Atlas booster and an Agena target vehicle.

This round of preparations had begun for Gemini 9 well before Gemini 8's trouble-shortened voyage. Gemini 9 had gone on the space-flight schedule as another rendezvous and docking mission. Before Project Apollo began, NASA wanted to practice those two important maneuvers several times. In addition, one of the Gemini 9 astronauts was to leave the spacecraft to test a new rocket-powered maneuvering pack that he would wear on his back.

Two astronauts who had never flown in space before were selected for Gemini 9. They were Elliot M. See, Jr., a 38-year-old former civilian test pilot, and Charles A. Bassett II, an Air Force captain who had also been a test pilot. Their backup crew was Thomas P. Stafford, the pilot of Gemini 6, and Eugene M. Cernan.

Gemini 9 was tentatively scheduled for May, 1966. During the months before the flight, the astronauts usually trained in Houston, but they also trained at Cape Kennedy and other places connected with the Gemini program. On February 28 they flew to the McDonnell Aircraft plant in St. Louis to inspect their Gemini 9 capsule and to rehearse the flight in McDonnell's Gemini simulator. The astronauts traveled to St. Louis in jet-powered T-38s—See and Bassett in one and Stafford and Cernan in a second.

The clouds were low when the T-38s approached the McDonnell landing field. See was at the controls of the leading plane; Stafford flew the other. Both pilots broke off their initial approach in the rain and fog. See circled the field once and started to land for a second time. As he came down, one of his wing tips hit the roof of a McDonnell building. The T-38 crashed, killing both the pilot and the copilot. A few minutes later Astronaut Stafford landed his T-38 safely.

See and Bassett were the second and third Project Gemini astronauts to be killed. In 1964 Astronaut Theodore Freeman had crashed to his death when he was disabled by a goose that smashed through the windshield of his T-38.

NASA names backup teams of astronauts so that its space missions can be carried out even if something happens to the primary crew. Consequently, preparations for Gemini 9 continued on schedule with Thomas Stafford as command pilot and Eugene Cernan as pilot. Astronaut James A. Lovell became the new backup command pilot and Astronaut Edwin E. Aldrin the backup pilot.

Like Gemini 8, Gemini 9 required a double launching— an Atlas-Agena combination from Pad 14 and a Titan-Gemini combination from Pad 19 an hour and 39 minutes later. After being boosted into orbit by the Atlas, the Agena would become a docking target for Gemini 9's astronauts. Each man was to practice docking at least twice. The astronauts also planned to use the Agena's power to maneuver the docked spacecraft.

The Atlas-Agena countdown on May 17, 1966, was the "smoothest ever." The Atlas' engines ignited on schedule and lifted the Agena up into the gray clouds. But two minutes and ten seconds after the launch, signals from the Atlas to the ground ceased abruptly. One of the booster's engines had suddenly gone wild, throwing the rocket into a tailspin. Engineers call such an engine failure a "hardover."

As a result of the hardover, the Atlas carried the Agena into the Atlantic Ocean instead of into orbit. Astronauts

Stafford and Cernan, waiting in Gemini 9, received the bad news from Mission Control: "We have lost our bird. The mission is scrubbed."

It was the third time that Tom Stafford had been sealed up in a Gemini capsule only to emerge again without having gone anywhere. On two different occasions his Gemini 6 flight had been postponed at the last minute. "I've been up here a number of times before," he said philosophically.

The two astronauts were going to get another chance to travel in space, however. Gemini 9 was rescheduled for two weeks later. It would take that long to install another Atlas on Pad 14. Because a second Agena would not be available in time, a substitute target vehicle would have to be used instead.

The substitute was the ATDA, for augmented target docking adaptor. It was developed as a stand-by replacement for the Agena after Gemini 6's Agena target vehicle failed to orbit. The ATDA had only limited power of its own. It would not be able to maneuver independently in space or propel the combined spacecraft after Gemini 9 docked with it.

Astronauts Stafford and Cernan climbed back into Gemini 9 on June 1. On Pad 14 the countdown for the Atlas-ATDA launch was already underway. Because of the change in the target vehicle, plans for the mission had been revised. They now called for three separate rendezvous maneuvers from far apart in space. There were to be nine dockings with the ATDA and Cernan was to leave the capsule for $2\frac{1}{2}$ hours during his second day in space.

While Gemini 9 astronauts lie ready in their capsule, technicians make final lift-off preparations in the White Room on June 1, 1966.

The Atlas left Pad 14 on schedule at 10 A.M. EST. It placed the ATDA in a circular orbit 185 miles above the earth's surface—just right for Gemini 9's first rendezvous maneuver. But Gemini 9 remained on Pad 19. Because of a mechanical failure, a computer inside the spacecraft failed to receive last-minute instructions for catching up with the ATDA. Gemini 9 could not leave without the instructions, so just two minutes before lift-off, its flight had to be canceled.

"I just can't believe it. I just can't believe it," the disappointed Eugene Cernan said when he learned the mission had to be called off. But it was quickly rescheduled for June 4. There would be two launch windows that day— one, for six minutes, beginning at 8:39 A.M. EST and the second, for 35 minutes, beginning at 10:15 A.M.

Gemini 9 got off the ground in time to use the first of the two launch windows. When it went into orbit, the ATDA was about 640 miles ahead of the spacecraft and 80 miles above it. During a four-hour chase, Stafford and Cernan were to adjust Gemini 9's orbit only three times. If all went according to plan, the final adjustment would move Gemini 9 into an orbit identical with that of the ATDA.

Officials at the Manned Spacecraft Center were worried about the ATDA, however. It left Pad 14 with a two-piece protective shroud of Fiberglas covering its docking collar. The shroud was to have been jettisoned before the ATDA went into orbit. If the shroud remained in place, docking would be impossible unless the astronauts could somehow remove it or signals from the earth to the ATDA could shake it loose. Ground instruments indicated that the shroud was still on the docking collar, but no one could be absolutely sure until the astronauts saw the ATDA.

It took Command Pilot Stafford just three orbits and three orbital adjustments to catch up with the ATDA. He closed in on it during the fourth hour of the flight, when the two craft were over the Pacific. As they approached their docking target, the astronauts could see the gaping, jaw-like halves of the shroud on the ATDA.

"Hawaii," Stafford radioed, "we've got a weird-looking machine here." He continued: "Both clam shells of the nose cone are still on, but they are wide open. . . . It looks like an angry alligator out there rotating around."

Upon hearing the bad news, ground controllers sent signals to the ATDA in an attempt to dislodge the shroud. When that failed, Tom Stafford suggested from Gemini 9: "We might put out our docking bar and go up and tap it." He also suggested that during the space walk Astronaut Cernan could cut the wires that held the shroud.

But docking had to be abandoned, at least for the time being, while Mission Control worked on the problem. Instead of docking, Gemini 9 drew away from the ATDA and then performed a successful rendezvous without the help of the space capsule's on-board radar.

That rendezvous was followed by an even more difficult one in which Gemini 9 moved toward its target from above rather than below. An alternative plan in the Apollo Project called for this maneuver. When astronauts approach the moon in their lunar landing vehicle, they might decide not to touch down after all. If that happens, the Apollo mothership will have to descend from its lunar orbit and pick them up.

Playing the part of the Apollo spaceship, Gemini 9 tried to track the ATDA from about 90 miles in front of it. The two astronauts found the ATDA very hard to see from above. When they searched the area where their radar told them the ATDA was located, they could see nothing in the glare of the sunlight reflected from the Atlantic Ocean and later from the Sahara Desert.

The "angry alligator."

Referring to the ATDA, Stafford said: "We cannot see him against the sunlit ocean below." A few minutes later he reported: "We're passing over the sand dunes of the Sahara, also some lava flows, and are looking straight down at him and I still can't see him."

They had traveled to within two or three miles of the ATDA before they managed to see it. "Finally have a little spot down there," Stafford reported then.

The astronauts closed in on the ATDA to take photographs and fly formation with it. When they finished the lengthy maneuver, the astronauts were, as Stafford put it, "pretty well bushed." And their fuel level was down to 11 per cent. Since safety required that they keep at least 5 per cent of their fuel in reserve, all hope of docking with the ATDA, or even flying formation with it again, was abandoned. Stafford moved Gemini 9 into a slightly different orbit and drew away from the target vehicle. When the astronauts last saw the angry alligator, it was several miles above and behind them, with its Fiberglas jaws still gaping wide.

Astronaut Cernan's extravehicular activity was the next item on the schedule for Gemini 9. When the time to begin preparations drew near, however, the tired astronauts decided to wait until the next day, and Mission Control agreed with their decision. The astronauts' physician, Dr. Charles Berry, was pleased with the decision too. "It's a red-letter day," he said. "I never heard a test pilot admit he was ever tired before." Dr. Berry pointed out that Project Gemini still had no clear idea of the "cost" of space travel and space work to an astronaut's physical and mental well-being.

After a good night's sleep, the astronauts were ready for $2\frac{1}{2}$ hours of extravehicular activity. The day started off with a problem, however. They had unpacked the EVA tether and reported, "We've got the big, black snake out of the black box," when their capsule began to roll in space. A ground engineer diagnosed the trouble at once— the capsule's No. 3 thruster. He told the astronauts what to do and the crisis ended.

When Stafford and Cernan finished their preparations, they depressurized the cabin. Then Cernan opened his hatch and stood up in his seat. "It sure is beautiful out here, Tom," he told his companion, who had to remain in the spacecraft.

One of Cernan's first extravehicular chores was to retrieve an emulsion pack from the outside of the spacecraft. It had been catching samples of space dust and microorganisms for scientists to study.

Then Cernan took some pictures—of Los Angeles, Lower California, Mexico, and of Astronaut Stafford. Stafford, in turn, took pictures of the space-walking Cernan. He did this with the help of a rear-view mirror which Cernan had mounted on the capsule's docking bar.

Like Astronaut Edward White, Project Gemini's first space walker, Cernan had trouble managing his 25-foot-long oxygen and communications line. At one point he complained: "The snake's all over me, Tom." Cernan soon learned that a short grip on the line gave him better control, but special grip pads on the cord proved ineffective. And, like Astronaut White, he had to constantly fight a tendency to float above the spacecraft. As he maneuvered about the capsule, Cernan paused to admire it. "Oh, what a beautiful spacecraft," he exclaimed.

After 55 minutes of space walking, Cernan moved back to Gemini's adapter. The spacecraft was approaching the dark side of the earth. While the astronaut waited for daylight, he planned to strap on the new jet-powered Astronaut Maneuvering Unit (AMU) that Gemini 9 carried in its adapter section. The AMU, a back-pack with armrests, would supply Cernan with oxygen, fuel, and communications. During the remainder of the space walk, it

A photo of Gemini 9 taken by Astronaut Cernan during his space walk. Note his tether curving down to the open hatch.

would enable the astronaut to move around without the help of the hand-held maneuvering gun that Ed White had used. And Cernan's only connection with the spacecraft would be a 140-foot tether.

When he reached the adapter, Cernan discovered that the AMU had not jettisoned its tublike protective cover. The astronaut removed the cover with some difficulty and began to prepare the AMU for the up-coming space walk.

Cernan's checklist contained 32 items, some of which required a surprising amount of effort in the weightless world of space. The astronaut began to breathe heavily and to perspire. When his spacesuit's evaporator unit could no longer remove all of the moisture, it condensed and then began to freeze on his cold faceplate.

Behind his fogged-up visor, Cernan could no longer tell which way was up—a very dangerous situation for a space-man to be in. After the flight, he recalled: "I looked into the black night, and the earth and the night looked the same. I could not see the horizon."

Communications between Cernan in the adapter and Stafford in the spacecraft were bad because the bulk of the capsule blocked their radio signals. Cernan managed to inform Stafford of his plight, however, and Stafford re-layed the information to the tracking station at Carnarvon: "He's fogging real bad. It's far more difficult than it was in the simulations."

Then he asked Cernan: "How you doing, Gene?"

"Really fogged up, Tom," was Cernan's discouraging reply.

When Gemini 9 approached Hawaii, Stafford informed the tracking station there: "It's four or five times more work than what we anticipated. And the pilot's visor is completely fogged over, nearly frozen over. Communications are very poor. He sounds like a loud gargle. If the situation doesn't improve, it's no go on the AMU."

Hoping to defog his faceplate, Cernan increased the flow of oxygen into his suit. The extra oxygen made no difference, and Cernan had to tell his command pilot that the situation had not improved. Stafford, in turn, radioed Houston: "No go for the AMU. The pilot's fogged up completely."

After a short rest, Cernan groped his way back to Gemini 9's open hatch. The spacecraft had moved into daylight again, but the heat of the sun failed to clear the astronaut's visor. With his vision reduced to a small area immediately in front of his nose, Cernan climbed back into the capsule. His extravehicular activity had lasted two hours and five minutes.

The astronauts spent their last night in space resting and taking pictures through the capsule's hatch windows. They were scheduled to land in the Atlantic Ocean the next morning.

Gemini 9's splashdown, only two miles from the carrier *Wasp*, was the first landing in the U.S. manned-space-craft program to take place before television cameras. The cameras were on the deck of the *Wasp* and they picked up Gemini 9 as soon as it appeared below the clouds. The Early Bird communications satellite trans-mitted the pictures to millions of American and European homes. Viewers saw the splashdown, and then the re-covery of the astronauts and their capsule by the *Wasp*.

Although the astronauts were disappointed that they had not been able to carry out all of the Gemini 9 mission, they were generally pleased with the results of their space flight. Stafford commented: "I think we learned a lot."

And Cernan said: "I'm coming back a lot smarter."

They had successfully demonstrated three new ren-dezvous procedures—locating a target vehicle in only three orbits; locating a target vehicle without the help

Splashdown

of radar; and locating a target vehicle from above. Gemini 9's two-hour-and-five-minute space walk had provided much useful information, and the capsule had made an extremely accurate landing.

As for the "failures" of Gemini 9—the canceled maneuvers and the shortened space walk—they could, and would, be tried again during the three Gemini missions still to be flown.

CHAPTER 9
Gemini Flies High

With the splashdown of Gemini 9, ending the program's seventh manned flight, Project Gemini entered its final stages. The approaching finish of the historic Gemini program brought with it no slackening of effort, however. On the contrary, flight plans became more ambitious than ever. There were still several things to be tested before Project Apollo began. And three vital space activities—rendezvousing, docking, and extravehicular activity—had to be practiced again.

Gemini 10, a three-day mission planned for July, 1966, had rendezvousing and docking as its primary goal. It was to be a very special kind of rendezvousing and docking, however. First, Gemini 10 would locate and dock with an Agena target vehicle launched especially for that mission. Then, using the Agena's propulsion system, Gemini 10 was to rendezvous with the Agena that had been orbiting the earth since the Gemini 8 mission in March. Before and after that very complicated space maneuver, there were to be periods of extravehicular activity.

Astronauts John Young and Michael Collins received the difficult Gemini 10 assignment. Young, who had served as the pilot on the Gemini 3 flight, was to be the command pilot this time. Astronaut Collins had never traveled in space before.

After six months of intensive training, the two astronauts reported to Pad 19 on the afternoon of July 18. There was to be a late afternoon launching because of the location in space of the old Gemini 8 target vehicle. But the old Agena 8 was only one of their targets. In order to rendezvous and dock with their first target, Agena 10, Young and Collins could be no more than 35 seconds late in leaving Pad 19. Even an extra second's delay would scrub the flight for at least 48 hours.

The dual launching of Agena 10 and Gemini 10 went off without a hitch. An Atlas booster lifted Agena 10 from Pad 14 at 3:39 P.M. EST. Gemini 10 followed from Pad 19 at 5:20 P.M., shortly after the Agena crossed Florida at the end of its first trip around the earth.

"Looking good!" reported the ground stations as Gemini 10 went into orbit. Agena 10 was 1,150 miles ahead of the space capsule, traveling in a nearly circular orbit that ranged from 183 to 187 miles above the earth. Gemini 10's orbit was lower—from 100 to 168 miles in altitude.

The astronauts executed their first rendezvous maneuver after two hours and 18 minutes of flight. They raised the perigee of Gemini 10's orbit from 100 to 134 miles. A few minutes later another burst from the thrusters changed the plane of the capsule's orbit to one identical with that of Agena 10. While these maneuvers were in progress, Gemini 10 continued to travel faster than the Agena because its orbit was lower.

As the distance between the two spacecraft narrowed, Gemini 10's radar began to search for the Agena. It locked on to the target vehicle when 280 miles separated them. Shortly thereafter, the astronauts moved Gemini 10 into the Agena's circular orbit.

Young and Collins were proving to be a notably uncommunicative pair of space travelers. They confined their conversations almost entirely to transmitting instrument readings and acknowledging messages from the ground.

When Gemini 10 passed over the tracking station at Tananarive in the Malagasy Republic during the fourth orbit, the flight plan called for the capsule to be station keeping with the Agena. But no message came from the astronauts. Finally, Gemini Control in Houston sent a message for Tananarive to relay to the spacecraft: "Are you there yet?" Mission Control asked.

The answer came back from Gemini 10: "Roger, we're there." After five hours and 21 minutes and 100,000 miles of space flight, Gemini 10 had arrived by its target vehicle.

Command Pilot Young flew near Agena 10 for 40 minutes. Then he maneuvered the spacecraft's nose into the Agena's docking cone. Project Gemini had achieved another perfect docking!

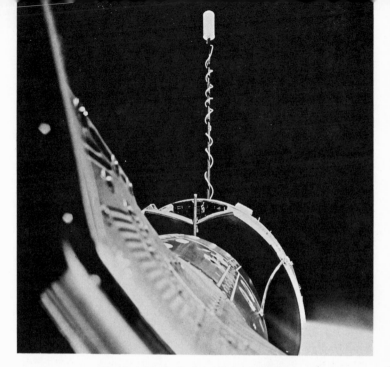

Gemini 10 docked with Agena 10.

Gemini 10's maneuvers had used up a great deal of fuel, however. Instead of having 680 pounds of fuel remaining after docking, as planned, the spacecraft had only 350.

While it remained docked to the Agena, Gemini 10 had no fuel problems. The 26-foot rocket carried ample fuel for its own 16,000-pound-thrust engine. Upon an electronic command from Astronaut Young, that engine raised the combined spacecraft into an orbit with an apogee 475 miles above the earth. The Agena engine fired only 14 seconds but it was enough to produce a comment from the usually silent Young. "That was really something," he exclaimed. "When that baby lights, there's no doubt about it."

Gemini 10 was now in the highest orbit ever attained by a manned spacecraft. The orbit was so high that the spacecraft traveled through a region known as the South Atlantic Anomaly. In that area, the Van Allen radiation belts dip unusually close to the earth. The radiation encountered by the astronauts was well within safe limits, however.

Gemini 10 remained in its high orbit during the astronaut's eight-hour sleep period. While they slept, Agena 8, at an altitude of 248 miles, moved ahead of the Gemini and Agena 10 combination.

The next day's maneuvers began with a thrust from Agena 10's big engine, this time for 11 seconds. It was a braking thrust that reduced Gemini-Agena's speed and lowered its orbit from 475 to 245 miles. A final thrust placed the docked spacecraft in a 240-mile circular orbit.

As they drew closer to the orbiting Agena 8, Astronauts Young and Collins prepared for their first period of extravehicular activity. It was to be a 70-minute stand-up EVA during which Michael Collins would open his hatch, stand up in his seat, and carry out some experiments from that position.

First, however, the silent spacemen received a suggestion from the Manned Spacecraft Center that they do a little more talking. The astronauts explained that they had been talking, but to Agena 10. "We have been pretty busy. This Agena takes a lot of talking to," they told Houston.

They did have some things to report. The 16mm movie camera on Collins' side of the spacecraft was broken. The usual annoying coating of launch exhaust gases had obscured the hatch windows. And they observed: "It will be

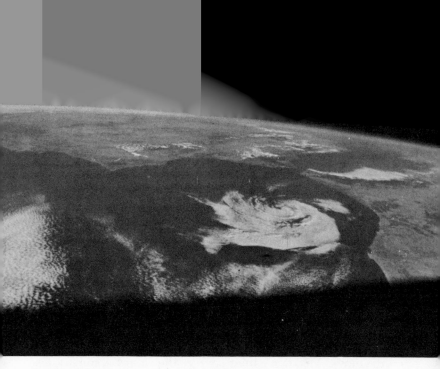

A storm-cloud vortex over the Atlantic, seen from Gemini 10 (looking toward the Straits of Gibraltar).

nice to get this door open to see what the world looks like. . . . We can just see a little piece of the ball. It looks pretty. It looks almost round from here."

A few moments later Astronaut Collins opened his hatch and stood up with his head and shoulders outside the de-pressurized spacecraft. Because Gemini 10 was traveling in darkness, Collins began his EVA by taking several pictures of the stars. When the spacecraft moved into day-light, he took pictures of patches of red, yellow, blue, and green that Gemini 10 had carried into orbit. From this experiment NASA hoped to learn what effect space had on color photography.

Suddenly Collins' eyes began to burn and water. He could barely see. Astronaut Young, who remained seated in the capsule, was experiencing the same difficulty. He quickly called Collins back inside. The astronauts then closed the hatch and repressurized the spacecraft.

Young and Collins reported the unexpected development to Houston: "The problem is something in the ECS system which caused our eyes to water to the point where we couldn't see."

The astronauts were referring to the spacecraft's environmental control system, which was supposed to supply them with pure oxygen to breathe. They thought that lithium hydroxide, a chemical used to absorb the carbon dioxide they exhaled, had somehow gotten into their oxygen lines. Gemini Control was inclined to agree with that diagnosis. Whatever their source, the fumes gradually disappeared when the capsule was repressurized, and the astronauts were able to finish the rest of the day's activities.

After a nine-hour sleep period, the busy spacemen began their preparations for the rendezvous with Agena 8. Using Agena 10's engine for the last time, Young moved the combined Gemini-Agena 10 spacecraft to a position 159 miles below and behind Agena 8. Then he undocked from Agena 10 and used Gemini 10's thrusters to move toward Agena 8. Agena 8 was a dead rocket. It had no power and its transponder—the automatic answering radar device—no longer worked. Without the help of the transponder, the astronauts had to rely on instructions from the ground and their own ability as navigators as they closed in on their second target vehicle.

The ground stations over which Gemini 10 passed picked up signals from the rendezvousing space capsule, but the astronauts sent few voice messages. After a long period of silence, Mission Control asked them: "See anything of the Agena 8 around?"

The calm voice of Astronaut Young answered: "Yeah, we are about, I guess, seven or eight hundred feet out."

"Fantastic, John!" exclaimed the surprised capsule communicator.

"Yes, I don't believe it myself," agreed the astronaut.

While Command Pilot Young moved closer to the Agena and flew in formation with it, Astronaut Collins finished preparations for his second period of extravehicular activity.

This time he left the spacecraft after he opened the hatch. His first stop was Gemini 10's adapter, where he plugged in the nitrogen line of his hand-held maneuvering gun. Nitrogen gas, passing through the gun's metering valves and nozzles, would supply a controlled thrust when the astronaut wanted to move about during his space walk. Then he returned to the hatch while Young moved Gemini 10 underneath Agena 8. When only five or six feet separated the two orbiting craft, Collins moved over to the Agena.

The space walker's objective was a micrometeorite package that had been collecting samples during Agena 8's four months in orbit. Collins removed the package from the Agena's hull and returned it to Astronaut Young in Gemini 10.

As Collins moved about outside the spacecraft, Young found that he had to make constant use of his thrusters to keep Gemini 10 stable. The capsule's fuel supply, already low, began to drop toward the danger point. With 15 minutes of the 55-minute space walk still to go, Mission Control told Young to use no more fuel. And Young, in turn, told Collins: "Come on back in the house."

Collins returned to the spacecraft bringing with him several pieces of equipment he had used, including his 50-foot tether. After closing the hatch and repressurizing the capsule, the astronauts sorted out the items they no longer needed. These they put into a large nylon bag. An hour later they reopened the hatch and let the bag float away. It would circle the earth in a gradually decreasing orbit and finally burn up when it plunged into the earth's atmosphere.

The spacecraft was now in order and the astronauts were ready for landing. First, however, they drew away from the Agena 8 and settled down for a last night of sleep in space.

Like the rest of the Gemini 10 mission, the landing on the morning of July 21 was a smooth one. The capsule came down less than three miles from the recovery ship *Guadalcanal*.

During its three days in space, Gemini 10 had set an altitude record for manned spacecraft. It had rendezvoused with two Agena target vehicles. It had docked with one of the Agenas and used the powerful Agena engine to maneuver in space. There had been two productive periods of extravehicular activity—one of them involving another orbiting vehicle.

With the experience gained from Gemini 10 to help

Gemini 11 Astronauts Conrad (front) and Gordon, leaving Pad 19 after the second postponement of their flight.

them, space officials completed preparations for Gemini 11. It was to be another three-day rendezvous-and-docking mission. But, once again, Project Gemini planned something a little different. The Gemini 11 astronauts, Charles Conrad, Jr., and Richard F. Gordon, Jr., were to rendezvous with an Agena rocket less than an hour after leaving Pad 19. If they were successful, they would rendezvous three hours sooner than any previous pair of astronauts had rendezvoused.

Charles Conrad had already spent eight days in space— as the pilot of Gemini 5 a year earlier, in August, 1965. For Richard Gordon, Gemini 11 was to be the first trip into space.

Conrad and Gordon's Gemini 11 mission had to be postponed twice. On September 9 a small leak in the Titan booster resulted in a one-day delay. Then a fault in the automatic-pilot system of the Atlas that was to lift the Agena target vehicle into orbit caused an additional two-day delay. But on the morning of September 12, the Atlas carried the Agena into a perfect orbit. Astronauts Conrad and Gordon left Pad 19 exactly 97 minutes and $24\frac{1}{2}$ seconds later. Their launch was only a half-second late.

When Gemini 11 went into orbit, it was 246 miles behind the Agena. Gemini 11's orbit was slightly lower than the Agena's orbit, however, so the spacecraft began to gain on its target vehicle.

With speed and precision, Command Pilot Conrad carried out a series of delicate maneuvers that carried Gemini 11 to the Agena. The astronauts had to make nearly all the tricky guidance calculations themselves. In a one-orbit rendezvous there wasn't time for ground stations to track the two spacecraft, feed the data to computers, and relay instructions to Gemini 11. The Gemini astronauts were also getting some good practice for the future. On the Apollo moonflights, astronauts will be too far from the earth to rely on ground-station computers.

The space flight was only 33 minutes old when Conrad and Gordon reported: "Be advised, we're inside of fifty miles and have the Agena in sight."

After Conrad moved closer to the Agena, he radioed the Manned Spacecraft Center: "Would you believe M equals one?" In the Gemini 11 flight plan the rendezvous assignment had been designated "M equals 1."

"Good show! Very nicely done! Outstanding!" replied the pleased ground controllers.

Gemini 11 had demonstrated that one spacecraft could catch up with another in less than one orbit. If an emergency occurred during a moon mission, the Apollo mothership might have to reach the lunar landing vehicle that quickly.

An hour and 34 minutes after launch, as it neared the end of its first orbit, Gemini 11 docked with the Agena. Following that initial docking, the astronauts carried out a series of maneuvers, including a redocking by Richard Gordon. He was the first Gemini copilot to practice docking.

A space walk by Astronaut Gordon was the big event of Gemini 11's second day in orbit. It turned out to be a very strenuous walk.

Before the walk began, Gordon paused to admire the view from his open hatch. "It's a beautiful day," he said. Then, while Conrad held his feet to keep him from drifting away, he retrieved an experiment package from the outside of the spacecraft. He also set up a movie camera to record his extravehicular activities.

As he prepared to leave the spacecraft, the astronaut found his 30-foot lifeline very difficult to manage. "I've got to rest here a minute," he told Conrad after struggling with the bulky tether.

The astronaut was breathing heavily, but he recovered after a short rest and left the spacecraft. He moved over to the Agena, which was still docked with Gemini 11. When Gordon reached the rocket, he had to rest again.

Astronaut Gordon astride the Agena.

The panting Gordon, sitting astride the Agena, reminded Astronaut Conrad of a cowboy riding a horse. "Ride it, cowboy," Conrad said to him.

Conrad also had some good advice for his copilot. "All right, just rest. You've got plenty of time. You've only been out for nine minutes," he told him.

Gordon rested for several minutes. Then he took one end of a 100-foot cord that the Agena carried under its docking collar and attached it to Gemini 11's nose. The bulk of the cord was to remain coiled up in the Agena until the two spacecraft separated. The astronauts would then fly formation with the entire 100 feet of the cord stretched between Gemini 11 and the Agena. If the cord kept the two spacecraft in position, it would save precious maneuvering fuel.

Astronaut Gordon managed to attach the cord to Gemini 11's nose. But the effort involved caused him to perspire profusely. He could not, of course, remove his visor to wipe his face and soon his right eye was blinded by perspiration. Gordon reported his disability to Command Pilot Conrad, who immediately called the space walker back into the capsule.

Then Conrad told the Tananarive tracking station: "I just called Dick back in. We are repressurizing the cabin right now. He got so hot and sweaty he couldn't see."

Gordon was tired as well as sweaty, but after resting he felt fine again. Undaunted by the sudden end of the space walk, the astronauts finished the day's schedule of activities and settled down for a sleep period.

Looking over the northwest coast of Australia from 850 miles up.

Gemini 11's third day in space was another busy one.
It began with a 25-second "burn" of the Agena's engine that
carried the combined spacecraft into an orbit with an 850-
mile-high apogee.

"We're on top of the world," Astronaut Conrad exclaimed as Gemini 11 soared past Gemini 10's record altitude. He described the view: "We're looking straight down over Australia now. We have the whole southern part of the world at one window. Utterly fantastic."

The astronauts could see millions of square miles of sea and continents from Australia to India.

After two trips around the earth following a path that carefully avoided areas of heavy radiation, the combined spacecraft returned to an orbit of 180 to 190 miles. In the new orbit Astronaut Gordon carried out a two-hour stand-up EVA. His second EVA was much less strenuous than the first one. The astronaut leisurely photographed the stars and carried out experiments while standing in his seat.

Later that day, Gemini 11 undocked from the Agena. As Conrad slowly backed the space capsule away, the 100-foot cord that Gordon had attached to Gemini 11's nose began to unreel. Instead of staying 100 feet apart, however, the two spacecraft tended to drift together while the slack tether rotated between them.

Conrad reported what was happening to the ground: "This tether is doing something I never thought it would do. It's like the Agena and I have a skip rope between us. We're skipping rope with this thing."

Finally, after some maneuvering with Gemini 11's thrusters, the astronaut was able to report: "It looks like we've got a good spin going." Gemini 11 and the Agena were rotating slowly in a 100-foot circle, once every nine minutes. The tether remained taut and the two spacecraft were stable. Aided by the tether, Gemini 11 was station keeping without using fuel to maintain its position.

The station-keeping experiment was the last big item on Gemini 11's schedule. The space mission ended the next morning with a spectacular computer-guided splashdown in the Atlantic. During the reëntry, Gemini 11's onboard computer fed commands directly to the spacecraft's thrusters. The astronauts monitored the computer closely, of course. They were ready to take over at once if they were needed. But the computer brought Gemini 11 down safely less than two miles from the recovery ship *Guam*.

Gemini 11 went on the record books as a very successful mission. Astronauts Conrad and Gordon had accomplished a first-orbit rendezvous-and-docking, high-altitude orbiting, and formation flying using a 100-foot tether. On the other hand, Gemini 11's shortened space walk caused considerable concern.

In discussing the problems presented by extravehicular activity, the Manned Spacecraft Center's director, Robert R. Gilruth, said: "We still have a lot to learn and we aren't quite sure what it is that we are missing. All the other tasks that we have set ourselves to do in Gemini seem to have yielded to the hard work that has gone into them. There has been a lot of hard work going into EVA, but it hasn't been as yielding as the other technical problems."

There was still a chance to try again, however. Three periods of extravehicular activity were scheduled for Gemini 12, Project Gemini's last mission.

A last look at the Agena after disconnecting the tether.

CHAPTER 10
The Final Mission

When Gemini 12 left Launch Pad 19 on November 11, 1966, it carried with it NASA's hopes for a solution to the space-walking problem. Although the flight plan for the last Gemini mission was a comprehensive one that included almost all the project's major objectives, space agency officials understandably placed special emphasis on the extravehicular part of the mission.

After reviewing the EVA experiences of Astronauts Edward White, Eugene Cernan, Michael Collins, and Richard Gordon, Project Gemini's flight planners had scheduled a number of basic EVA tasks for Gemini 12. While the tasks were being performed, studies would be made of the stresses and strains they caused. From those studies NASA hoped to learn what work astronauts should and should not attempt to do outside of a space capsule as well as what equipment was most helpful.

The Gemini 12 astronauts, Command Pilot James A. Lovell, Jr., and Pilot Edwin (Buzz) Aldrin, had trained diligently for their important mission. Lovell was a veteran of the 14-day Gemini 7 flight. Aldrin, a space rookie, was scheduled to perform Gemini 12's extravehicular activity. Part of his preparation for the EVA assignment took place underwater in a swimming pool. The buoyancy of the water made the astronaut feel almost as weightless as he would in space. Wearing his pressure suit, he worked on a mock-up of the Gemini capsule while color cameras recorded his movements.

After two one-day delays caused by malfunctions in the guidance system of the Titan 2 booster, Gemini 12 began its trip into space at 3:46 P.M. EST on November 11. An Agena target vehicle, launched an hour and 38 minutes earlier, was already orbiting the earth. Both launches had gone off without a hitch, but trouble soon struck Gemini 12. The mission's first major activity was a rendezvous and docking with the Agena. The astronauts had planned to use radar to locate the Agena, but Gemini 12's radar wasn't working. Undaunted, Lovell and Aldrin combined their own keen vision with skillful flying to find the target vehicle. Successfully using what astronauts call the "eyeball" method, they linked up with the Agena during the third orbit, as scheduled.

After the docking, the flight plan called for the Agena's engine to lift the combined spacecraft into a 460-mile-high orbit. When the time came to perform that maneuver, controllers on the ground advised the astronauts not to start up the Agena's powerful engine. Tracking stations had received signals that indicated something was wrong with the Agena's fuel pump.

Rather than risk the chance of an explosion in space by trying to use the Agena engine, the controllers gave Gemini 12 another assignment—one that had been dropped from the original Gemini flight plan when the mission was delayed for two days. By carefully firing the Agena's small engines, the astronauts could move the combined spacecraft into the path of a rare total eclipse of the sun, and they were told to do just that. It meant maneuvering to a precise spot in the Pacific off the coast of Peru at the moment when the moon began to move between the earth and the sun.

"So that eclipse got to us after all," Lovell remarked when he received the new instructions.

First, however, the astronauts had a sleep period. They started it an hour early because they were to be awakened two hours earlier than usual to prepare for the eclipse. In addition to maneuvering into position, they had to mount two 16mm cameras and one still camera. They also put a shade over one hatch window and installed a filter on the other to guard against eye damage.

The total eclipse on November 12, 1966, was the first of its kind in 18 months and only the thirty-ninth since 1900. It began at dawn over the Pacific Ocean west of the Galapagos Islands and ended in the Atlantic southeast of Brazil. An estimated 800 scientists were in South America to photograph and study the mysterious corona of gases surrounding the sun. The corona is best observed during the few moments of a total eclipse.

One hundred and seventy miles above the scientists, Astronauts Lovell and Aldrin in Gemini 12 took pictures while the moon slipped across the face of the sun and during the seven or eight seconds of total eclipse. Their pictures would not be obscured by the haze of the earth's atmosphere, as would pictures taken on the ground. The astronauts also tried to photograph the 55-mile-wide shadow of the moon as it traveled across South America. Astronaut Lovell told Mission Control in Houston: "We hit the eclipse right on the money, but we were unsuccessful in picking up the shadow."

"Roger," answered Mission Control, "we figured it would be a long way off."

After shooting the first pictures ever taken from space of a total eclipse of the sun, the astronauts turned to the next item on their schedule. It was a very important part of the mission—a stand-up EVA by Astronaut Aldrin.

While still seated Aldrin began his activity with 30 seconds of calisthenics, during which he moved his hands back and forth from his lap to his helmet at the rate of once a second. As he did this, his pulse and respiration readings were recorded for later study.

After completing the exercises Aldrin stood up in his seat. A short tether held him in place while he mounted an ultraviolet camera on the side of the spacecraft. The astronaut's major assignment during this EVA was to take pictures of the ultraviolet rays emitted by certain stars. From the pictures scientists hoped to gain information about how stars are formed.

At first Aldrin couldn't locate the stars he was to pho-

Astronaut Aldrin with the ultraviolet camera in his right hand, during stand-up EVA.

tograph because Gemini 12 was flying through daylight. The astronauts did see a number of pieces of space debris, however. "Seems there's a good amount of garbage up here," Lovell reported to the ground. "Things are floating all around us."

When Gemini 12 moved into darkness, Aldrin was able to locate and photograph two of three star fields. In addition to taking pictures, the astronaut attached a handrail to the outside of the capsule for the next day's space walk. And he retrieved two glass-like strips that had been mounted behind the spacecraft's hatch to record any contamination by rocket fumes.

While he worked, Aldrin talked with Lovell and with the ground stations over which he passed. Before taking a picture of Texas, he told the Mission Control Center at Houston: "Tell everybody to smile down there."

When Aldrin described the "beautiful view" to Lovell, that veteran space traveler replied: "What did I tell you, Buzz? Four days' vacation with pay and see the world."

At one point Lovell had to caution Aldrin about where he put his feet as he leaned out of the spacecraft. "Watch it, watch it," Lovell said. "Get your foot out of the way. You've got it on the switch for the fuel cells."

After standing in the open hatch for two hours and 29 minutes, Aldrin returned to his seat in the cockpit and the astronauts repressurized the capsule. In Houston, Flight Director Glynn Lunney announced that he was pleased with Aldrin's physical reaction during the space stand. "His heart rate and respiration were very low during the whole thing," Lunney reported.

Astronaut Aldrin worked outside the spacecraft again the next day. This time he left the capsule, although he remained connected to the spacecraft by a 25-foot life line that supplied him with oxygen and carried his messages. The astronaut wore a 42-pound chest pack, which contained an emergency supply of oxygen and a special unit to absorb moisture from his breath and perspiration. He was also equipped with some new restraining devices because previous space walkers had found it very difficult to remain in position while working in the weightless void outside the capsule.

Gemini 12 was to repeat Gemini 11's tethered station-

keeping experiment. To prepare for it, Aldrin moved over
to the Agena, which was still docked with the Gemini
spacecraft. Steadied by two short nylon tethers fastened to
his parachute harness and to the Agena, the space walker
retrieved one end of a 100-foot cord and attached it to
Gemini's nose. As he worked Aldrin did not experience
the exhaustion that had handicapped Astronaut Richard
Gordon during the Gemini 11 mission. Aldrin's tethers
helped him maintain his position, he used a simpler method
of attaching the cord to Gemini 12, and he rested fre-
quently.

After another short rest period Aldrin moved toward
Gemini 12's adapter. To keep from floating away from
the spacecraft he used the handrail he had installed the
previous day and two Velcro hand pads and a series of
Velcro patches. His hand pads looked like cement trowels.
When he pressed them against the Velcro patches on the
spacecraft, tiny hooks enmeshed with pile material and
held the pads to the patches.

At the adapter Aldrin slipped his feet into two large
gold shoelike restraints. (They were painted a gold color
to reflect heat.) He also connected his two nylon tethers
to the spacecraft. After a rest period the astronaut went
to work on a 30-by-30-inch panel on which were mounted
fixed and removable bolts, hook and ring combinations,
and a set of electrical plugs and cables. While he turned
bolts, snapped hooks through rings, and plugged in electrical cables, the astronaut experimented with his foot
restraints and his tethers. He used each system alone and
carefully observed how it maintained his body position.

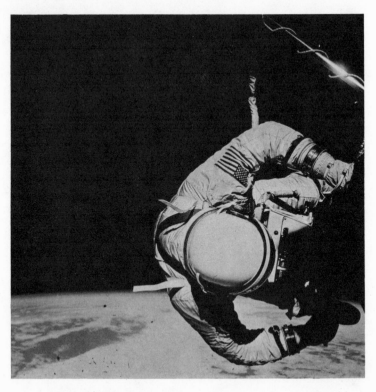

Aldrin gropes his way along the docked spacecraft.

The use of restraints, along with frequent rest periods, was making Aldrin's space walk much less arduous than Gemini's earlier walks. Aldrin did not become over tired, he did not perspire heavily, and his visor did not fog up. Furthermore, he completed all of his EVA assignments.

The astronaut's last task before getting back into his seat and closing the spacecraft hatch was to detach the handrail and toss it out into space. As he did so, he remarked: "I'm the world's highest javelin thrower."

Edwin Aldrin was also the world's champion space walker. His two-hour-and-nine-minute walk was four minutes longer than Astronaut Eugene A. Cernan's walk during the Gemini 9 mission. With his space stand, Aldrin's extravehicular activity totaled a record four hours and 38 minutes.

During the space walk Gemini 12 had remained docked with the Agena. After the walk the astronauts were scheduled to perform the station-keeping experiment with the 100-foot tether connecting Gemini 12 and the Agena. To get ready for the experiment, Lovell and Aldrin undocked from the target vehicle and climbed slightly above it. As Gemini moved away, it pulled the tether out of a storage bag in the Agena's nose.

At first the line connecting the two spacecraft would not remain taut. Instead, it lashed back and forth and even wrapped around the Agena. During the Gemini 11 station-keeping experiment, Astronauts Conrad and Gordon had faced a similar problem. And like the Gemini 11 astronauts, Lovell and Aldrin finally stabilized the tether. They used a different station-keeping technique, however. Instead of slowly rotating in a 100-foot circle with the Agena, they kept Gemini 12 slightly above the Agena with Gemini's nose pointing at the Agena's nose and the earth. The very slight difference in the pull of gravity on the two craft was enough to keep them 100 feet apart and no manuevering fuel had to be used to maintain their positions.

With its nose pointed toward earth, Gemini 12 flies in formation with the tethered Agena.

At the end of the station-keeping experiment, Gemini 12 pulled away from the Agena and the astronauts settled down for their third night in space. The next morning they were awakened early to look for a yellow cloud of sodium vapor over the Sahara. The vapor came from French rockets launched from Algeria as Gemini 12 passed overhead. The launching was a French-American experiment designed to measure wind speeds in the upper atmosphere.

After Gemini 12's first pass over the Sahara, Astronaut Lovell reported: "We sure looked and just goggled all ways, but we didn't see a thing."

During the next orbit the astronauts tried again, but Lovell had to report: "We saw no cloud. Pictures taken, but no observation."

Astronaut Aldrin continued Gemini 12's picture taking after he opened the spacecraft's hatch later that morning for another stand-up EVA. He photographed the star fields Gamma Velorum and Orion and a sunrise over the Indian Ocean. When he took pictures of the sunrise, Aldrin protected himself from the sun's blinding rays by remaining behind the hatch cover and shooting over his shoulder. He explained: "It was a little difficult to get the shots of the sunrise. . . . They were kind of backhanded shots. . . . I think we ought to get some good pictures of it."

Before the end of the 60-minute EVA, the astronauts jettisoned the garbage and excess equipment that had accumulated in their cabin. Then they closed the hatch and repressurized Gemini 12 for the last time.

Lovell and Aldrin had been experiencing control problems as they orbited the earth. Three of the spacecraft's

16 maneuvering jets were no longer working. The problem was not serious, although it did result in a high rate of fuel consumption. After the stand-up EVA they put Gemini 12 into drifting flight to save fuel. And plans for a second rendezvous with the Agena were abandoned.

As their last full day in space drew to a close, the astronauts did a few more experiments and listened to music beamed to the spaceship's radio frequency by Mission Control in Houston. Meanwhile, in the primary Atlantic recovery area—about 700 miles southeast of Cape Kennedy—a force of ships, planes, and helicopters moved into position, headed by the aircraft carrier *Wasp*. Project Gemini's last flight was almost over.

The next afternoon, after 59 revolutions of the earth and 94 hours in space, Gemini 12 splashed down into the Atlantic at 1:22 EST. The computer-controlled landing was just three miles from the *Wasp*. Within minutes a recovery helicopter had reported: "No difficulties. The astronauts have signaled they are all O.K."

The Gemini 12 astronauts had added several new items to Project Gemini's already long list of achievements. Pilot Edwin Aldrin's space walk was the longest and the first completely successful working space walk. His total time outside the spacecraft—$5\frac{1}{2}$ hours—set a record. Command Pilot James Lovell's total time in space—425 hours and 8 minutes—set another record. The astronauts took the first pictures from space of a solar explipse, but that was just one of their photographic accomplishments. The 500 still pictures and 1,000 feet of movies that they brought back were the best of any of the Gemini missions.

Pararescuemen wait with the Gemini 12 capsule while the Wasp *approaches.*

Showing no ill effects from their four days in space, Lovell and Aldrin traveled to the *Wasp's* flight deck in a helicopter. After a welcome from the crew and NASA officials, the astronauts began a busy schedule that included thorough medical examinations, dinner on the *Wasp*, and a flight back to Cape Kennedy the next morning for conferences and more examinations.

At Cape Kennedy workmen were preparing to dismantle Pad 19. Some of its equipment would be used for other space programs and the rest would be scrapped. Many of the technicians who had helped make Project Gemini a success had already started to work on other projects. And the Gemini astronauts, who had solved so many problems for Project Apollo, were now Apollo astronauts.

With the successful conclusion of its twelfth flight, the Gemini program was over. During the two years that Gemini capsules orbited the earth to help prepare for a manned landing on the moon, the United States' capability in space had increased tremendously.

Gemini astronauts had practiced rendezvousing and docking, maneuvers upon which the success of Project Apollo depends. They proved that men could travel and work in space for at least 14 days—twice the length of time required for a trip to the moon and back. They explored the mysteries of extravehicular activity. They learned how to make precise landings from space. And they tested new equipment as well as new space-travel techniques. Gemini's astronauts tried out pressure suits, fuel cells, chest packs, hand-held maneuvering units, body restraints, on-board computers, and dehydrated foods. There were advances on the ground, too, during the course of Project Gemini. The number of days required to prepare for a spacecraft launching was reduced drastically. At the same time, preflight and launch operations became so efficient that lift-off often occurred within a fraction of a second of the scheduled time.

Project Gemini was a space program that accomplished or exceeded every one of its objectives, and space scientists agree that it was well worth the 1.35 billion dollars it cost. Before going to the moon the United States had to learn to operate in space. Project Gemini provided that information in abundance.

CHAPTER 11
Americans on the Moon

The long-awaited day has arrived at last. The attention of the whole world is focused on NASA's John F. Kennedy Space Center on Merritt Island, just northwest of Cape Kennedy. The space center covers 88,000 acres of what was once farmland. Citrus trees still grow on some of its many acres, but Merritt Island has become the gateway to the moon. From the space center's huge Launch Complex 39, American astronauts are about to embark on a momentous lunar journey.

Three astronauts have already entered the cone-shaped command module of a Project Apollo spacecraft. The command module, which is the top section of the spacecraft, measures 13 feet in diameter at the base and 12 feet from base to top. There is room inside for three astronauts to work, eat, and sleep. They do not have to wear pressure suits in the crew cabin. In addition to housing the astronauts, the command module serves as the spacecraft's control center.

Apollo has two other sections. One, called the service module, carries some of the breathing oxygen, electrical power supplies, and other items not needed directly within the pressurized crew cabin. It also provides propulsion for Apollo's maneuvers in space. The service module is located beneath the command module as the spacecraft sits on the launching pad.

The third section of the Apollo is an adapter which connects the spacecraft with the booster. It contains the 12-ton lunar module, or LM.

The launching of Project Apollo's first attempt to land men on the moon is still some minutes away, but the astronauts are already far above the ground. Their space capsule, perched on top of its giant Saturn 5 booster, is as high as the thirtieth story of an average skyscraper. The combined height of the Apollo mooncraft and the Saturn is 362 feet, more than three times the height of the Gemini-Titan combination.

The Saturn, under development since 1958, is the United States' first large booster. Its first stage has five engines that give it $7\frac{1}{2}$ million pounds of thrust. The first-stage fuel tanks carry over 200 tons of liquid oxygen and kerosene. The booster's second stage has five engines with a total thrust of one million pounds. Its fuel is liquid oxygen and liquid hydrogen. The Saturn 5's third stage has a single engine producing 200,000 pounds of thrust. Like the second stage, it uses oxygen and hydrogen fuel.

Because of their huge size, the three stages of the Saturn 5 could not be delivered to Merritt Island by land or air. Instead they arrived by barge and were assembled

in the moonport's Vehicle Assembly Building. Like every-thing else at the moonport, the Vehicle Assembly Building is big. It is 716 feet long, 515 feet wide, and 525 feet high —the largest building in the world in terms of volume.

Technicians assembled and checked out the Saturn 5 and the spacecraft for this first manned Apollo moon mis-sion on a mobile launcher, in one of the Vehicle Assembly Building's four huge bays. The moonport has three mobile launchers, each one 446 feet high and a half acre in area. They contain their own computer facilities, instrumentation equipment, and communications systems. Except for their huge size and the fact that they are movable, they re-semble ordinary launch pads.

A crawler-transporter, the world's largest land machine, moved the mobile launcher and the Saturn-Apollo to Launch Complex 39, $3\frac{1}{2}$ miles from the Vehicle Assembly Building. The crawler-transporter has a top speed of only one mile an hour, but it can carry 12 million pounds. It moves on eight huge tracked crawlers, two at each of its four corners. The road, or crawlerway, that it uses is as wide as an eight-lane highway. The crawler-transporter also moved a 40-story mobile service structure to the launch site. Technicians used the mobile service structure to make final checks on the booster and the spacecraft. When the technicians finished their checks, the crawler-transporter moved the mobile service structure away.

Inside the Apollo spacecraft the astronauts have com-pleted their own last-minute checks as the countdown moves

A full-scale model of the Apollo spacecraft. The lower section holds the lunar landing module.

into its final minutes. Launch Control, which for Apollo is located near the Vehicle Assembly Building, transmits a last message: "All systems are GO for the blast-off."

With a tremendous roar the first stage of the Saturn 5 lifts the 3,000-ton booster-spacecraft combination away from Launch Complex 39. America's first moon explorers are on their way.

Like the Gemini spacecraft, the Apollo spacecraft has an escape system. It is designed to rocket the command module and its occupants to safety in case of a booster failure. Today, however, the moon-bound travelers do not need to use it. The Apollo's dials and gauges tell them that both the spacecraft and the booster are performing well.

Two and a half minutes after launch the Saturn's first stage exhausts its fuel, shuts down, and separates from the booster-spacecraft combination. Then the second stage ignites and lifts the spacecraft until it too burns out and separates.

A few minutes later the single engine of the Saturn's third stage injects the Apollo into an earth orbit. The engine shuts down and the booster-spacecraft combination circles the earth for one and a half orbits while the astronauts test the equipment they will be using during the next part of their journey. When the tests are completed, they restart the engine and head for the moon.

Approximately two hours later the Apollo's command and service modules move away from the Saturn's burned-out third stage. The two modules turn around and dock nose-to-nose with the lunar landing module, which is still attached to the Saturn. The booster is then abandoned and the docked spacecraft resumes its flight to the moon, using the service module's rocket engine.

From the command module the astronauts take bearings on the stars to help them guide the spacecraft. They also use Apollo's computer and other navigation and guidance equipment. Although all systems are being monitored on earth, as they travel they doublecheck both their own physical condition and the condition of the spacecraft systems. They send frequent reports to the earth.

When they are within 80 miles of the moon, the astronauts use the service module's engine to brake the spacecraft and inject it into a lunar orbit. The three astronauts travel around the moon for a while, studying its surface. Then two of them crawl through a hatch into the lunar module's two-man cabin. After checking out the LM's equipment, they separate from the mothership.

Using the LM's variable-thrust engine, the two astronauts begin the final descent to the lunar surface. At 300 feet they hover and examine landing sites along the lunar equator. They look for a level area with a smooth surface. They must avoid mountainous terrain and areas strewn with boulders. If they decide not to land, they can rocket back to the mothership. But they spot what appears to be a safe landing place and gently set the LM down on its four extendable landing legs.

Not quite 75 hours have passed since the launching from Complex 39. It is sunrise on the moon. The time was selected to protect the explorers from the intense cold of the lunar night, when temperatures drop as low as minus 262 degrees Fahrenheit.

A scale model of a landing on the moon.

For the next six hours the astronauts explore the moon in the vicinity of their landing site. They collect samples of dust, soil, pebbles, and small rocks from the lunar surface. They make measurements, perform experiments, and take pictures. Because the moon is so much smaller than the earth, the distance to the horizon and the area the astronauts can see are reduced accordingly. But the absence of atmosphere makes visibility very good. Everything within the astronauts' line of vision is new and interesting; and they are very busy.

Following a six-hour rest period inside the LM, the astronauts explore the moon for another six hours. Then they start up the LM's 3,500-pound-thrust ascent engine. Leaving the vehicle's legs and descent engine behind, they climb into a lunar orbit. There they rendezvous and dock with the Apollo mothership.

After the two moon explorers have crawled back into the command module, the LM is abandoned in space and Apollo heads for home with its full crew of three astronauts. Power is supplied by the service module's engine, which accelerates the spacecraft from a 4,000-mile-per-hour lunar orbit into a 6,000-mile-per-hour earth trajectory.

On its return journey, Apollo does not go into orbit around the earth. Instead, it heads directly for a reëntry "corridor." Before reëntry begins, the astronauts jettison the service module and rotate their capsule to place its blunt end forward. Like the Mercury and Gemini capsules, Apollo carries on its blunt end special protection against the searing heat of reëntry. Three parachutes break the moonship's fall as it approaches its Pacific landing area and drop it gently into the water.

When that landing takes place, the space goal President Kennedy set for the United States in 1961 will have been realized. Americans will have traveled to the moon, done some exploring of its surface, and returned to earth.

Before that first trip to the moon, however, other astronauts will prepare the way by orbiting the earth and the moon to test Apollo equipment. And unmanned exploratory spacecraft have already begun to provide much valuable information about the moon.

Project Apollo's first big test took place on February 26, 1966, when an unmanned moonship made a successful 5,300-mile suborbital flight over the South Atlantic. A two-stage Uprated Saturn 1, the Apollo test-program booster, lifted the spacecraft from Merritt Island's Launch Complex 34, the Saturn 1 launching area. Forty minutes later Apollo, powered by its own engine, hurtled down into the ocean after reaching a height of 310 miles. It successfully withstood the 5,000 degrees of blistering heat generated during its reëntry into the earth's atmosphere at a speed in excess of 18,000 miles an hour.

Project Apollo took its second big step toward the moon on August 25, 1966. It was another unmanned, suborbital flight, but this time the spaceship traveled three-quarters of the way around the world to land in the Pacific Ocean southeast of Wake Island. The Saturn's second stage and the spaceship's own engine carried it to a peak altitude of 706 miles. The Apollo engine passed its restart test by igniting four different times. The flight also tested the Apollo's heat resistance and fuel cells, as well as guidance, navigation, and communications systems.

After the unmanned tests, flights with three-man teams of astronauts are scheduled to begin. The first of these will be earth-orbit missions using the Uprated Saturn 1. Then the giant Saturn 5 booster will carry astronauts into earth orbit and possibly into lunar orbit. During these flights the

The first unmanned Apollo shot, launched on February 26, 1966.

astronauts will practice rendezvousing, docking, and other maneuvers that will be used in reaching the moon.

While its manned space program moves toward the goal of a landing on the moon, NASA is collecting information about the moon from its three unmanned lunar exploratory programs—Ranger, Surveyor, and Lunar Orbiter.

A photo of the lunar crater Copernicus, transmitted by Lunar Orbiter 2.

The pioneer Ranger program, which began in 1959, has produced some remarkable photographs of possible landing areas on the moon, as well as valuable scientific information. Ranger cameras took their pictures before the spacecraft made a "hard," or crash, landing.

Surveyor spacecraft have braking rockets which enable them to make "soft" landings. As a result, Surveyor cameras can take pictures after landing, as well as during the lunar approach. The detailed pictures and other information transmitted by Surveyors will help determine the landing site of the first manned Apollo moon mission.

NASA's Lunar Orbiter will help select landing areas for both Surveyors and Apollo LMs by transmitting photos from a low lunar orbit. Lunar Orbiters will also collect general scientific data.

Like the United States, the Soviet Union plans to land men on the moon. And the Soviet Union has been gathering information about the moon in much the same way. Its Lunik 2, which crash-landed on the moon on September 13, 1959, was the first spacecraft to reach the moon. The Soviet Luna series of space vehicles transmits pictures from a lunar orbit. Lunas are also capable of making soft landings on the moon.

The National Aeronautics and Space Administration is gathering information about conditions on the moon; astronauts are in training; the spacecraft and the booster are almost ready. Americans are preparing to go to the moon.

And after the first lunar landing?

There will still be a great deal to learn about the moon. Astronauts might make an extensive survey of the moon from a lunar orbit. Or, supported by supplies deposited in advance, they might land and explore the moon for several days.

The powerful Saturn-Apollo combination can also be used for earth-orbit projects, such as manned space stations. The space stations could serve as astronomical observatories, as communications links, and as centers for gathering information about the earth's resources.

And after astronauts have explored the moon and established earth-orbiting space stations?

Just as Project Gemini prepared the way for a landing on the moon, the experience gained from Apollo and its follow-up projects will open the way to manned exploration of the rest of the solar system.

APPENDIX
The Gemini Astronauts

The National Aeronautics and Space Administration's astronaut program began in 1958 with a search for the nation's very best military test pilots. The seven men who were chosen became the Project Mercury astronauts.

NASA decided to limit its selection to test pilots for several reasons. Test pilots were familiar with fast, high-altitude aircraft, which they often flew under difficult conditions. Test pilots also possessed the necessary engineering training, and they were men with the proven ability to act quickly, and correctly, in an emergency. Military test pilots had the additional advantage of being readily available for assignment to NASA, and their very complete military records made the selection process easier.

With the groups of astronauts chosen in 1962 and 1963, however, NASA opened its program to civilians as well as military test pilots. And in 1965 the first scientist-astronauts were chosen. Three of the astronauts who flew Gemini missions, Virgil Grissom, Gordon Cooper, and Walter Schirra, had participated in Project Mercury. The other astronauts who flew Gemini missions were selected from the groups chosen in 1962 and 1963.

All astronauts take part in an intensive training program. In addition, each man specializes in the development of one or more areas of manned space flight.

Edwin E. Aldrin, Jr.

The pilot of the Gemini 12 mission was born in Montclair, New Jersey, on January 20, 1930. After graduation from the United States Military Academy in 1951, Aldrin joined the Air Force and received his wings the next year. He flew 66 combat missions in Korea as a member of an F-86 jet fighter squadron. He is credited with two enemy aircraft destroyed and one damaged.

Following the Korean War, Aldrin was a gunnery instructor, an administrative assistant at the Air Force Academy, and a flight commander in a tactical fighter wing. In 1963 he received a doctor of science degree in astronautics from the Massachusetts Institute of Technology. He wrote his doctoral thesis on guidance systems for manned orbital rendezvous.

When he was selected for the astronaut training program in 1963, Aldrin was on the staff of the Air Force Field Office at NASA's Manned Spacecraft Center. As an astronaut he has specialized in mission flight planning for both the Gemini and Apollo programs.

In addition to serving as the pilot of the Gemini 12 mission, Air Force Lieutenant Colonel Aldrin was backup pilot for Gemini 9.

Neil A. Armstrong

One of the first civilian test pilots chosen for the astronaut program, Neil Armstrong was born in Wapakoneta, Ohio, on August 5, 1930. Although he was a civilian when selected as an astronaut in 1962, Armstrong had served as a naval aviator from 1949 to 1952. He flew 78 combat missions during the Korean War.

As a civilian test pilot, Armstrong flew experimental planes for the Lewis Flight Propulsion Laboratory (now NASA's Lewis Research Center) and the NASA High Speed Flight Station at Edwards Air Force Base in California. At Edwards he helped test the X-1 and X-15 rocket airplanes; the F-100, F-101, and F-102 jet fighter planes, and the B-47 jet bomber.

Astronaut Armstrong has specialized in the development, design, and use of trainers and simulators. He was the command pilot of the Gemini 8 mission that accomplished the first docking in space. He was also backup pilot for Gemini 11.

Armstrong has a bachelor of science degree in aeronautical engineering from Purdue University.

Frank Borman

The command pilot of the history-making Gemini 7 mission was born in Gary, Indiana, on March 14, 1928. The future astronaut attended high school in Tucson, Arizona, and entered the Air Force after graduation from the United States Military Academy in 1950.

Borman became a fighter pilot and served with several fighter squadrons. In 1957 he received a master's degree in aeronautical engineering from the California Institute of Technology. He then became an instructor in thermodynamics and fluid mechanics at the Military Academy.

Prior to his selection as an astronaut in 1962, he was an instructor at the Aerospace Research Pilot School at Edwards Air Force Base in California.

Borman, an Air Force colonel, has specialized in NASA's booster design and development program.

Eugene A. Cernan

Navy Commander Eugene A. Cernan was born in Chicago, Illinois, on March 14, 1934. He received a bachelor of science degree in electrical engineering from Purdue University.

While at Purdue, Cernan joined the Navy Reserve Officers' Training Corps. He entered naval flight training after graduation and served with Attack Squadrons 126 and 113 at the Miramar, California, Naval Air Station. Before becoming an astronaut in 1963, Cernan earned a master of science degree in aeronautical engineering at the United States Naval Postgraduate School at Monterey, California.

Cernan was the pilot of the Gemini 9 mission and the backup pilot for Gemini 12.

Michael Collins

Air Force Lieutenant Colonel Michael Collins was born in Rome, Italy, on October 31, 1930. Like several of his fellow astronauts, he chose the Air Force as a career when he graduated from the United States Military Academy.

Before his selection as an astronaut in 1963, Collins was an experimental flight-test officer at the Air Force Flight

Test Center at Edwards Air Force Base. At the Center he tested performance, stability, and control characteristics of Air Force planes, primarily jet fighters.

In addition to serving as the pilot of the Gemini 10 mission and backup pilot for Gemini 7, Collins has specialized in the development of pressure suits.

Charles Conrad, Jr.

One of Project Gemini's most active astronauts, Navy Commander Charles Conrad served as pilot of the Gemini 5 mission, backup command pilot for Gemini 8, and command pilot for Gemini 11.

Conrad was born in Philadelphia, Pennsylvania, on June 2, 1930. He attended Princeton University, graduating in 1953 with a bachelor of science degree in aeronautical engineering.

After graduation Conrad joined the Navy and became a naval aviator. He attended the Navy Test Pilot School at Patuxent River, Maryland, and became a test pilot and later a flight instructor and performance engineer at the Test Pilot School.

Prior to his selection as an astronaut in 1962, Conrad was safety officer for Fighter Squadron 96 at the Miramar, California, Naval Air Station. As an astronaut he has specialized in cockpit layouts, instrument displays, and pilot controls.

L. Gordon Cooper, Jr.

Air Force Colonel L. (for Leroy) Gordon Cooper was born in Shawnee, Oklahoma, on March 6, 1927. He served in the Marines and attended the University of Hawaii before becoming an Air Force pilot.

After flying F-84 jet fighters for four years, Cooper was assigned to the Air Force Institute of Technology, where he earned a bachelor's degree in aeronautical engineering. He then attended the Air Force Experimental Flight Test School at Edwards Air Force Base. After graduation he served as an aeronautical engineer and test pilot.

Cooper was one of the seven Project Mercury Astronauts. On May 15-16, 1963, he piloted the Mercury spacecraft, Faith 7, on a 22-orbit mission. After transferring to Project Gemini, Cooper became the command pilot for the eight-day Gemini 5 mission. He was also the backup command pilot for Gemini 12.

Richard F. Gordon, Jr.

The pilot and space walker of the Gemini 11 flight was born in Seattle, Washington, on October 5, 1929. In 1951, after graduating from the University of Washington with a bachelor of science degree in chemistry, the future astronaut began his training as a naval aviator.

Gordon flew with an all-weather squadron before attending the Navy Test Pilot School. As a test pilot he worked with several of the Navy's jet fighter planes.

In 1961 Gordon won the Bendix Trophy race, flying from Los Angeles to New York in two hours and 47 minutes. He set a new speed record of 869.74 miles per hour.

Prior to becoming an astronaut in 1963, Gordon attended the Naval Postgraduate School.

Commander Gordon has specialized in cockpit layouts,

instrument displays, and pilot controls. In addition to taking part in the Gemini 11 mission, he was the pilot of the Gemini 8 backup crew.

Virgil I. Grissom

The command pilot of the first manned Gemini flight was born in Mitchell, Indiana, on April 3, 1926. He graduated from Purdue University with a bachelor of science degree in 1950, joined the Air Force, and won his wings in 1951.

Lieutenant Colonel Grissom, who was called "Gus" by his friends, flew 100 combat missions in Korea. After the Korean War, he became a jet instructor before studying aeronautical engineering at the Air Force Institute of Technology. He then attended test pilot school at Edwards Air Force Base and became a test pilot specializing in fighter planes.

Grissom was one of the Project Mercury astronauts selected in 1959. He flew a suborbital Mercury mission on July 21, 1961. His Gemini 3 flight on March 23, 1965, was a three-orbit mission. Astronaut Grissom was killed in a flash fire aboard an Apollo spacecraft on January 27, 1967, during a simulated countdown.

James A. Lovell, Jr.

Navy Captain James A. Lovell, Jr., was born in Cleveland, Ohio, on March 25, 1928, but he grew up in Milwaukee, Wisconsin. He began his military career at the United States Naval Academy, graduating in 1952 with a bachlor of science degree.

Following flight training, Lovell served in a number of

naval aviator assignments including a three-year tour as a test pilot at the Naval Air Test Center at Patuxent River, Maryland.

When he heard that NASA was looking for astronauts for Project Mercury, Lovell sent in his application. He was not selected then, but he was included in the group of astronauts selected in 1962.

Lovell was the pilot of the record-setting Gemini 7 mission and command pilot of Gemini 12. In addition, he has specialized in the design and development of recovery systems and systems connected with astronaut comfort, such as oxygen, food and water supplies, waste management, and odor control.

James A. McDivitt

Air Force Lieutenant Colonel James A. McDivitt was born in Chicago, Illinois, on June 10, 1929. He earned a bachelor of science degree at the University of Michigan, graduating first in his class.

McDivitt, who joined the Air Force in 1951, flew 145 combat missions in Korea.

The future astronaut received his test-pilot training at the Air Force Experimental Flight Test School and the Air Force Aerospace Research Pilot School. He served as an experimental test pilot at Edwards Air Force Base.

After his selection as an astronaut in 1962, McDivitt specialized in the design and development of guidance and navigation systems for the Gemini and Apollo spacecraft and the development of the command and service sections of the Apollo spacecraft. He was the command pilot of the Gemini 4 mission.

Walter M. Schirra, Jr.

The command pilot of the Gemini 6 flight was born in Hackensack, New Jersey, on March 12, 1923. He graduated from the United States Naval Academy in 1945 and received his flight training at the Naval Air Station, Pensacola, Florida.

As an exchange pilot with the Air Force, Schirra flew 90 combat missions in Korea. After the Korean War he took part in the development of the Sidewinder missile and the F7U3, a Navy fighter plane. He also served as an instructor pilot and as operations officer on the carrier *Lexington*.

When Schirra was selected as a Project Mercury astronaut in 1959, he had completed test-pilot training and was working with the Navy's F4H fighter.

Naval Captain Schirra's skillful piloting of his six-orbit Project Mercury mission and his successful rendezvous during Gemini 6 have earned him a reputation as a "textbook" pilot. He has specialized in overall operations and training.

David R. Scott

Air Force Lieutenant Colonel David R. Scott was born in San Antonio, Texas, on June 6, 1932. He earned a bachelor of science degree at the United States Military Academy and both a master of science degree in aeronautics and astronautics and an engineering degree in aeronautics and astronautics at the Massachusetts Institute of Technology.

Scott also graduated from the Air Force Experimental Flight Test School and the Air Force Aerospace Research Pilot School.

After becoming an astronaut in 1963, Scott specialized in the development of guidance and navigation systems. He was the pilot of the Gemini 8 mission that accomplished the first successful docking in space.

Thomas P. Stafford

Since becoming an astronaut in 1962, Air Force Lieutenant Colonel Thomas P. Stafford has been the backup pilot for the Gemini 3 mission, the pilot of Gemini 6, and the command pilot of Gemini 9.

Stafford was born in Weatherford, Oklahoma, on September 17, 1930. He joined the Air Force after his graduation from the United States Naval Academy in 1952. Following flight training and service as a fighter pilot, the future astronaut became a test pilot and a director of test-pilot training.

Stafford was a student at the Harvard Graduate School of Business Administration when he was selected for astronaut training. Since then he has specialized in the design and development of communications and instrumentation systems.

Edward H. White II

Project Gemini's first space-walker was born in San Antonio, Texas, on November 14, 1930. He joined the Air Force when he graduated from the United States Military Academy in 1952.

After winning his wings, the future astronaut flew fighter

planes before attending the Air Force Test Pilot School. As a test pilot at Wright-Patterson Air Force Base, Ohio, White made flight tests for research and weapons systems development, wrote engineering reports, and made recommendations for improving aircraft design and construction. After becoming an astronaut in 1962, Lieutenant Colonel White specialized in the design and development of flight control systems and related equipment.

In addition to his degree from the Military Academy, the astronaut held a master of science degree in aeronautical engineering from the University of Michigan.

White was killed in a flash fire on January 27, 1967, while carrying out a simulated countdown in an Apollo capsule.

John W. Young

Navy Commander Young was born in San Francisco, California, on September 24, 1930. He attended the Georgia Institute of Technology, earning a bachelor of science degree in aeronautical engineering.

After his graduation in 1952, Young entered the Navy. He became a test pilot, and in 1962 set world time-to-climb records in the 3,000 meter and 25,000 meter altitudes, flying the F4B Navy fighter.

Young became an astronaut in 1962. He was pilot of the Gemini 3 mission, backup pilot for Gemini 6, and command pilot of Gemini 10. In addition he has specialized in environmental control systems, pressure suits, survival gear, and associated pilot equipment such as spacecraft ejection seats.

Manned Space Flights

Flight   *Date*

Vostok 1 (USSR)   April 12, 1961
  Carried Cosmonaut Yuri A. Gagarin. Landed after one revolution.

Mercury-Redstone 3
  (USA)   May 5, 1961
  Carried Astronaut Alan B. Shepard. Landed after a 15-minute
  suborbital flight.

Mercury-Redstone 4
  (USA)   July 21, 1961
  Carried Astronaut Virgil I. Grissom. Landed after a 15-min-
  ute suborbital flight.

Vostok 2 (USSR)   August 6–7, 1961
  Carried Cosmonaut Gherman S. Titov. Landed after 17.5
  revolutions.

Mercury-Atlas 6 (USA)   February 20, 1962
  Carried Astronaut John H. Glenn, Jr. Landed after three revolutions.

Mercury-Atlas 7 (USA)   May 24, 1962
  Carried Astronaut Scott Carpenter. Landed after three revolutions.

Vostok 3 (USSR)   August 11–15, 1962
  Carried Cosmonaut Andrian G. Nikolayev. Landed after 64
  revolutions.

Vostok 4 (USSR)   August 12–15, 1962
  Carried Cosmonaut Pavel R. Popovich. Came within three
  miles of Vostok 3 on initial orbit. Landed after 48 revolutions.

Mercury-Atlas 8 (USA)   October 3, 1962
  Carried Astronaut Walter M. Schirra, Jr. Landed after six
  revolutions.

Flight   *Date*

Mercury-Atlas 9 (USA)   May 15–16, 1963
    Carried Astronaut L. Gordon Cooper, Jr. Landed after 22
    revolutions.

Vostok 5 (USSR)   June 14–19, 1963
    Carried Cosmonaut Valery F. Bykovsky. Landed after 81
    revolutions.

Vostok 6 (USSR)   June 16–19, 1963
    Carried Cosmonaut Valentina V. Tereshkova, the first female
    space traveler. Passed within three miles of Vostok 5. Landed
    after 48 revolutions.

Voskhod 1 (USSR)   October 12–13, 1964
    Carried Cosmonaut Vladimir Komarov; Konstantin Feoktistov,
    a scientist and spacecraft designer; and Boris Yegorov, a
    physician. Landed after 16 revolutions.

Voskhod 2 (USSR)   March 18–19, 1965
    Carried Cosmonauts Pavel Belyayev and Alexei A. Leonov.
    Leonov left spacecraft for 10 minutes. Spacecraft reached
    record height of 308 miles. Landed after 17 revolutions.

Gemini 3 (USA)   March 23, 1965
    Carried Astronauts Virgil I. Grissom and John W. Young.
    Landed after three revolutions.

Gemini 4 (USA)   June 3–7, 1965
    Carried Astronauts James A. McDivitt and Edward H. White
    II. White left spacecraft for 23 minutes. Landed after 62
    revolutions.

Gemini 5 (USA)   August 21–29, 1965
    Carried Astronauts L. Gordon Cooper, Jr., and Charles Con-
    rad, Jr. Set manned duration record—190.9 hours in space.
    Landed after 120 revolutions.

Gemini 7 (USA)   December 4–18, 1965
    Carried Astronauts Frank Borman and James A. Lovell, Jr.
    Set new manned duration record—330.5 hours in space.
    Landed after 206 revolutions.

Flight   *Date*

Gemini 6 (USA)   December 15–16, 1965
Carried Astronauts Walter M. Schirra, Jr., and Thomas P.
Stafford. Performed first rendezvous in space (with Gemini 7).
Landed after 15 revolutions.

Gemini 8 (USA)   March 16, 1966
Carried Astronauts Neil A. Armstrong and David R. Scott.
Performed first docking in space (with Agena target vehicle).
Landed after 6.5 revolutions.

Gemini 9 (USA)   June 3–6, 1966
Carried Astronauts Thomas P. Stafford and Eugene A. Cernan.
Performed three separate rendezvous and two hours and five
minutes of extravehicular activity. Landed after 44 revolutions.

Gemini 10 (USA)   July 18–21, 1966
Carried Astronauts John W. Young and Michael Collins. Performed rendezvous and docking and 87 minutes of extravehicular activity. Used Agena target vehicle engine to reach
record 475-mile altitude. Landed after 43 revolutions.

Gemini 11 (USA)   September 12–15, 1966
Carried Astronauts Charles Conrad, Jr., and Richard F. Gor-
don, Jr. Performed first-orbit rendezvous and docking and
two hours and 47 minutes of extravehicular activity. Used
Agena engine to climb to new record altitude of 850 miles.
Landed after 44 revolutions.

Gemini 12 (USA)   November 11–15, 1966
Carried Astronauts James A. Lovell, Jr., and Edwin E. Aldrin,
Jr. Performed rendezvous and docking and a record five hours
and 38 minutes of extravehicular activity. Landed after 59
revolutions.

Index

About the Author

Gene Gurney, a lieutenant colonel in the U.S. Air Force, has been a military pilot for 24 years and a command pilot for 12 years. He was born in Fremont, Ohio, and graduated from the University of Maryland.

During World War II, Lieutenant Colonel Gurney flew P-40 and P-38 fighters and B-24 and B-17 bombers. After the war he was an Air Force Counter-Intelligence Corps Special Agent investigating espionage, sabotage, and gold smuggling in the Near East and Europe. Later, while serving with the Strategic Air Command, he was the first combat crew member to fly the KC-135 jet tanker. In 1958 he was a pilot on the KC-135 that set a transcontinental speed record of three hours and 42 minutes during a flight from Los Angeles to New York. He is presently serving as a public information officer on the staff of the commander in chief of the Pacific Air Forces. He makes frequent visits to the combat air bases in Vietnam.

Gene Gurney is the author of 20 books, including two other popular Landmark Books for young readers: *Americans into Orbit* and *Flying Aces of World War I*. With Colonel Carroll V. Glines he has written a book about the Civil Air Patrol, *Minutemen of the Air*.

Lieutenant Colonel Gurney and his wife Clare have a home on Chesapeake Bay near Prince Frederick, Maryland.